THE LORE OF

LARGE NUMBERS

NEW MATHEMATICAL LIBRARY

published by

Random House and Yale University

for the

Monograph Project

of the

SCHOOL MATHEMATICS STUDY GROUP†

EDITORIAL PANEL

† The School Mathematics Study Group represents all parts of the mathematical
profession and all parts of the country. Its activities are aimed at the improvement
of teaching of mathematics in our schools. Further information can be obtained
from: School Mathematics Study Group, Drawer 2502 A, Yale Station,
New Haven, Connecticut.

THE LORE OF
LARGE NUMBERS

by

Philip J. Davis

National Bureau of Standards

He telleth the number of the stars;
He calleth them all by their names.
Psalm 147

6

RANDOM HOUSE

Illustrations by the author and Carl Bass

First Printing

Library of Congress Catalog Card Number: 61-13842

Manufactured in the United States of America

Note to the Reader

This book is one of a series written by professional mathematicians in order to make some important mathematical ideas interesting and understandable to a large audience of high school students and laymen. Most of the volumes in the *New Mathematical Library* cover topics not usually included in the high school curriculum; they vary in difficulty, and, even within a single book, some parts require a greater degree of concentration than others. Thus, while the reader needs little technical knowledge to understand most of these books, he will have to make an intellectual effort.

If the reader has so far encountered mathematics only in classroom work, he should keep in mind that a book on mathematics cannot be read quickly. Nor must he expect to understand all parts of the book on first reading. He should feel free to skip complicated parts and return to them later; often an argument will be clarified by a subsequent remark. On the other hand, sections containing thoroughly familiar material may be read very quickly.

The best way to learn mathematics is to *do* mathematics, and each book includes problems, some of which may require considerable thought. The reader is urged to acquire the habit of reading with paper and pencil in hand; in this way mathematics will become increasingly meaningful to him.

For the authors and editors this is a new venture. They wish to acknowledge the generous help given them by the many high school teachers and students who assisted in the preparation of these monographs. The editors are interested in reactions to the books in this series and hope that readers will write to: Editorial Committee of the NML series, in care of THE INSTITUTE OF MATHEMATICAL SCIENCES, NEW YORK UNIVERSITY, New York 3, N.Y.

The Editors

CONTENTS

LIST OF ILLUSTRATIONS
AND TABLES

Figure

Figure

Preface

The numbers have always been a source of wonder, and the sequence of integers whose unending procession is contrasted with the finiteness of human experience is surely the first place where mathematics appears as the product of soaring imagination. Children as well as adults raise many questions about large numbers. It has been my idea to answer these questions and at the same time to reveal a bit of the modern mathematical horizon via such questioning.

I have used the idea of large numbers as a binding theme for this book and, employing only the simplest materials, have tried to produce a feeling for numbers, their magnitude, and their growth. By means of approximate computation and estimation, I have suggested that numbers may be handled lightly and efficiently as friends with whom one discourses rather than as enemies against whom one struggles. In the later sections, large (and small) numbers take their place in mathematics and science, and are presented in a way which anticipates certain developments in abstract algebra and analysis and numerical analysis. I have tried to intimate—and this also has been a major aim—that mathematics is a living thing that grows and changes with the generations.

The problems are an integral part of the book. This does not mean that they must all be worked or be handled in the same manner. Some are meant to be read for they drive home a point or contain additional lore. Some are meant to be grappled with. Some require proofs, a word that should be interpreted flexibly. Some require additional information which the student must seek out for himself. For the most part, the problems can be worked with arithmetic alone, but this is not a text book and there are no "boxed methods" to serve as a complete guide. Every book should contain something for the reader to grow on; I have therefore included material in Part II which is more advanced, but which should not be allowed to impede the flow of the narrative.

To a certain extent this book is a family document. It was conceived the day I was asked by my children "What comes after millions?" It was begun after the question had been revised to "What comes after billions?" I hope with them, as with all who may be attracted to this book, that they will first grow into it and then grow out of it, and through it to the fertile acres of mathematical thought.

I should like to express my thanks to the School Mathematics Study Group for including this book in its monograph series, the *New Mathematical Library*, and to the Editorial Panel for many fine suggestions. Several discussions with Dr. Karl Goldberg during the initial writing were very helpful. Thanks are due also to Mrs. Molly F. Hevenor for helping with the secretarial work. I am grateful also to the editorial staff of the *New Mathematical Library* for its assistance, and particularly to Mrs. Jacqueline Lewis for her preparation of "Answers to Selected Problems."

Philip J. Davis

Chevy Chase, Md.
April, 1961

To Ab and Frank
who asked the questions
and
to Handy
who helped shape the answers

PART I

Large Numbers and Their Arithmetic

1. Numbers in the World

Today's world is a world of numbers. From morning to midnight men, women, and children are surrounded by numbers of all kinds. Mr. Green wakes up at 7 in the morning. He calls down to his wife that he'd like a 3 minute egg. He reads in the paper at breakfast that Pride's Folly came in 2nd in the Florida Handicap and paid $3.30 and that the temperature went down to −30° in Winnipeg. Mr. Green lets a number 22 bus go by and catches a number 44 bus into town. At a conference called for 10:00 A.M. his associates agree to put in a bid for $675,000 to carry out a construction job. Out of conference, Mr. Green tells his secretary to get him reservations for the 28th, 29th, and 30th of the month in Chicago. On his way home, he reads that the ABC foundation will spend $25,000,000 next year on school improvement and that the cost of living index rose .2 % over what it was a year ago. He recalls that his wife called at 4 and told him to stop at the pastry shop on his way home and buy a dozen rolls and a pound cake. The shop is crowded; he awaits his turn by getting a queue card labelled No. 71. As he opens the door to his house, his daughter tells him that she received an 85 in a spelling test.

And so it goes; numbers, numbers are everywhere. Numbers are found in greater and greater profusion with hardly a moment to think about them. Mr. Green is a lawyer, yet his day is full of numbers.

← Figure 1. Numbers in the world

5

Had he been an engineer, a scientist, a mathematician, a financier, his day might have been more so. What do they all mean? What purpose do they serve?

Problem Set 1

1. Open the daily paper to the front page and see how many numbers you can find there.
2. Think over what you did today and make a list of the various numbers that you had to deal with in one way or another. Do not count any numbers that may have arisen in your arithmetic or mathematics studies.

2. The Principal Uses of Numbers

If you examine the numbers that occur in daily life and look carefully at how they are used, you will soon discover that there are three principal uses. There are numbers used to express quantity: $25,000,000, 85 on a spelling test. These numbers are called *cardinal numbers*. They answer the questions: How much? How many? Cardinal numbers are frequently added, subtracted, multiplied, and divided one by another.

There are numbers which are used to express order in a sequence of things. Pride's Folly came in 2nd in a series of horses. Mr. Green was 71st in a series of pastry patrons. Such numbers are called *ordinal numbers*. They answer the questions: How far along in a line? Before or after? Ordinal numbers are merely compared with one another to determine which of two precedes or follows the other.

Finally, there are numbers which, like people's names, are used only to identify different objects. The number 44 bus goes over route number 44 and the number 22 bus goes over route 22. Such numbers may be called *tag numbers* or *identification numbers*. Tag numbers answer the question: Which one of many? Two tag numbers are merely compared with one another to see whether they are the same or different. We do not do the same things with them that we do with cardinals or ordinals. The number 44 bus is not costlier, faster, later, or twice the size of the number 22 bus. It is simply a bus that goes over a certain fixed route, which is *different* from the number 22 bus.

Sometimes the same number may be employed in several different ways. When Mr. Green draws the number 71 card in the pastry shop, this is usually an ordinal to him. It tells him that he must wait until his number is called up. To the lady behind the counter, this number may serve as a cardinal. She may say to her assistant, "We've had a busy day today. Do you realize that we've had 71 customers since 4 o'clock?"

Cardinals, ordinals, and tags; these are the three uses of numbers. Examine how a number is combined with other numbers and you will discover to which use it is put. If it is added, subtracted, multiplied, or divided it is used as a cardinal. If it is compared, it is used as an ordinal. If it is identified, it is a tag.

Type	Question Answered	Operations Employed	Symbols
Cardinals	How much?	Addition, Subtraction, Multiplication, Division	$+, -,$ $\times, \div$
Ordinals	How far along in a sequence?	Greater Than Less Than	$>$ $<$
Tags	Which of many?	Equals Does not equal	$=$ $\neq$

Figure 2. The principal uses of numbers

Problem Set 2

1. Does the following statement make any sense to you? "On a certain day the temperature at the South Pole station was $-15°$. One week later the temperature had doubled." What kind of numbers do you think Fahrenheit temperatures are?

2. *The Piccadilly Panhandle.* Many years ago a disabled veteran was begging in the famous Piccadilly Circus of London. Apparently, he was very successful for many people were seen to go over to him and read a sign he carried. They laughed and gave him money. This is what the sign said:

HELP!	WARS	3
	BATTLES	6
	WOUNDS	8
	MEDALS	3
	WIFE	2nd
	CHILDREN	8
	TOTAL	30

What sense does this sum make?

3. On the package of a breakfast food called Bita-Crix it is stated that 1 oz.
will provide the following percentages of daily adult requirements:

25 % of Thiamine

4 % of Riboflavin

4 % of Niacin

6 % of Calcium

12 % of Phosphorus

12 % of Iron

These figures total 63 %. Can you conclude from this that 1 oz. of
Bita-Crix satisfies 63 % of the nutritional requirements of an adult?

3. The World of Numbers

The world of nature is full of surprises. The Australian platypus is
a mammal which lays eggs. There are birds and fish with mysterious
migratory habits that are scarcely understood. The world of numbers
is likewise full of surprises, and finding out what they are is one of
the pleasures of studying mathematics.

One, two, three, four, five, ... These numbers are the ordinary
numbers of counting. Mathematicians call them the *positive integers*.
Integer is a word which comes to us from the Latin and means
"whole." The integers are the whole numbers and this book will for
the most part be about such numbers.

But the world of numbers has other species in it. Not all numbers
are whole. There are *fractions* such as $\frac{1}{2}, \frac{1}{3}, \frac{2}{13}, \frac{278}{451}$. There are *decimals*
such as 3.2, 44.8, .06. Decimals are really nothing but a convenient
way of writing special fractions whose denominators happen to be 10
or 100 or 1000, etc. Not all numbers are positive. It is frequently
useful to talk about *negative numbers:* The temperature in Winnipeg
was −30°. A debt of $100 may be represented as −$100. The
year 44 B.C. might be thought of as −44.

Not all numbers are positive or negative fractions. In plane geometry we learn that a square whose side is one foot long has a diagonal
which is $\sqrt{2}$ feet long. This number is called the *square root* of 2
and it is the number which, when multiplied by itself, produces 2.
It was known to the Greek mathematician, Pythagoras, who lived
in the year −500 (how many years ago was this?), that $\sqrt{2}$ cannot
be a fraction, that is, a whole number divided by a whole number.
There is a legend which says that when Pythagoras and his followers
discovered this upsetting fact, they offered up a considerable sacrifice
to the gods. Numbers that can be expressed as the ratio of two whole

numbers are called *rational*, and those that cannot are called *irrational*.†

Geometry also produced a second famous irrational number. If a person knows the diameter of a circle, how can he compute the length of its circumference? The proportion of the circumference to the diameter is always the same no matter how large or small the circle is. It is a number which is designated by the Greek letter π, and it is irrational. In a later portion of this book we shall have a lot to say about π.

Figure 3. $\pi = 3.141592653589793 \ldots$

The mathematical world of numbers, then, has whole numbers both positive and negative, fractions both positive and negative, irrational numbers both positive and negative. Each type has certain characteristics and identifying features. But there are even more types.

There are *complex numbers* such as $2 + 4\sqrt{-1}$ or $\frac{6}{7} + 2\sqrt[4]{-1}$. The complex numbers are able to express both quantity and direction. They have the peculiar property that if we have two of them, we can not say which is the larger.

There is a kind of quantity known as a *matrix* which is very important in many phases of science today. A matrix is really a rectangular array of numbers. They can be added to one another,

$$\begin{bmatrix} 0 & 6 & 2 \\ -1 & 4 & 0 \\ 0 & 2 & 3 \end{bmatrix} \qquad \begin{bmatrix} 1 & 1 & 1 & \frac{1}{2} \\ 2 & 2 & 1 & 0 \\ 3 & -1 & 4 & -\frac{1}{2} \end{bmatrix}$$

Figure 4. Quantities within quantities. Two matrices

subtracted, and multiplied according to special rules which are studied in Higher Algebra. Frequently, but not always, they can be

† See *Numbers: Rational and Irrational*, by I. Niven, this series.

divided. They have the disagreeable (and important) property that when two of them are multiplied together, it may make a difference as to the *order* in which the multiplication is carried out! When we multiply ordinary numbers, it makes not one whit of difference whether we take 4×7 or 7×4. Not so with matrices. The order is very important.

The integers, the fractions, the irrational numbers, the complex numbers, the matrices. Here, in increasing order of complexity, are the principal types of numbers which occur in mathematics today. Man has not always known about them. The integers predate history. The fractions occur in the earliest of Egyptian mathematical works (2000 B.C.). The irrationals, as we have seen, date from about 500 B.C. The complex numbers date from the 1500's. The matrices are scarcely more than 100 years old. The famous mathematician Leopold Kronecker who lived in the middle of the 1800's summed it up by saying that the integers were created by God and all the other types of numbers are the work of man. As mathematics and science progress together, other types of numbers will surely be invented and become important.

Problem Set 3

1. Take a large circular object such as a juice can or a lamp shade. With a tape, measure the diameter of the circle. Then wrap the tape measure around the circle and measure its circumference. Divide the second number by the first. Your answer is an "experimental" value of π. How close is it to the mathematical value?

2. *The Drunken Sailor.* A sailor walks 3 blocks north, 2 blocks east, 4 blocks south, 5 west, 2 south, 7 east, 8 north, and finally 4 west. Describe where he is at the end of this walk. See if you can invent a quick way of solving this kind of problem.

3. Multiply 1.414 by itself. How close to 2 is your answer? Try it with 1.4142.

4. Writing Numbers

Numbers serve a variety of purposes, some very simple, some quite complicated. The manner in which numbers are written is related to the use to which they are put. For very simple uses, practically anything will do, but for complicated ones, the manner of writing must be carefully worked out so that the numbers are easy to handle.

A western rancher wishes to distinguish his cattle from those of other ranchers by a special mark. There is no question of counting the brands of cattle or of putting them in a certain order, and therefore any mark will do as long as it is distinguishable from other such marks.

A state wishes to issue license plates to car owners so that the cars can be identified. Some states use ordinary numbers. Other states have a system which combines numbers and letters. For instance, all the numbers from 1 to 99,999 are used, and for the "higher" numbers a letter is added on the far left. Thus: P69,328 or X16,253. Sometimes the letter may be a special mark to designate a certain type of vehicle, a certain location, or a certain type of driver such as a doctor. These numbers are really tag numbers; no arithmetic needs to be performed on them, and so the letters cause no difficulties.

Today, numbers for general arithmetic use are written in the *decimal* system, a system based upon tens. This is the culmination of varieties of experience with numbers by many peoples over many centuries. The ancient Babylonians who lived in the 7th and 6th centuries B.C., and who were excellent computers, had a system of numerals which was based upon 60's. The Romans, much later, had their own peculiar way of writing numbers with letters. These Roman fossils can still be found on the faces of clocks, on the façades of public buildings, on chapter headings; and they are learned in grade school. Here are some samples as a reminder:

$$1 = I$$
$$2 = II$$
$$4 = IV$$
$$1955 = MCMLV.$$

The rules of number formation are quite helter-skelter, and real difficulties emerge when arithmetic must be performed with them. (See Problems 9 and 10 of Set 4.) The Romans managed to do arithmetic with them, but they probably used a kind of abacus to help them out whenever they bogged down in letters.

Another survival of an ancient number system is the British system of money. British money is measured in terms of pounds (£), shillings (s), and pence (d); twenty shillings to the pound, twelve pence to the shilling. British school children must learn special rules for dealing with arithmetic of money.

The decimal system, which has been in common use throughout the West for about 800 years, has earned its popularity for it has many attractive features. In this system, fundamental quantities are distinguished and given special symbols or marks. The quantities are zero, one, two, three, four, five, six, seven, eight, and nine. The special symbols, as you know, are 0, 1, 2, 3, 4, 5, 6, 7, 8, and 9. These symbols are called the *digits*, and all other numbers are written as combinations of these fundamental digits. As examples:

$$1,955 = \text{one thousand, nine hundred and fifty-five}$$

$$6,039,241 = \text{six million, thirty-nine thousand, two hundred and forty-one.}$$

$$8,629,798,478,111 = \text{eight trillion, six hundred twenty-nine billion, seven hundred ninety-eight million, four hundred seventy-eight thousand, one hundred and eleven.}$$

Notice how cumbersome it is to write out a large number in words. Counting the commas which are important to keep matters straight, the last number written out in words takes 127 symbols, but written in digits, it takes only 17 symbols. More than a 7 fold saving! One of the things that science must do is to condense its ideas and findings. Our number system is one of the first examples of such condensation.

What, a little more precisely, does a number such as 6,039,241 mean? In order to elaborate its meaning, special attention must be paid to certain distinguished numbers other than the digits. They are one, ten, one hundred, one thousand, ten thousand, etc. These numbers are the successive *powers* of ten. In the next section the idea of powers will be explained in considerable detail. For the moment, merely notice that

$$\text{one} = 1 = 1$$
$$\text{ten} = 10 \times 1 = 10$$
$$\text{one hundred} = 10 \times 10 \times 1 = 100$$
$$\text{one thousand} = 10 \times 10 \times 10 \times 1 = 1,000$$
$$\text{ten thousand} = 10 \times 10 \times 10 \times 10 \times 1 = 10,000$$
$$\text{one hundred thousand} = 10 \times 10 \times 10 \times 10 \times 10 \times 1 = 100,000$$
$$\text{one million} = 10 \times 10 \times 10 \times 10 \times 10 \times 10 \times 1$$
$$= 1,000,000 .$$

As we proceed from one line to the next we merely add on a zero to our previous answer.

These special numbers form a sequence of graduated reference numbers in terms of which other numbers can be expressed. For instance, the number 6,039,241 means

$$6 \times 1{,}000{,}000 = 6{,}000{,}000$$
$$\text{plus } 0 \times \quad 100{,}000 = \quad 000{,}000$$
$$\text{plus } 3 \times \quad 10{,}000 = \quad 30{,}000$$
$$\text{plus } 9 \times \quad 1{,}000 = \quad 9{,}000$$
$$\text{plus } 2 \times \quad 100 = \quad 200$$
$$\text{plus } 4 \times \quad 10 = \quad 40$$
$$\text{plus } 1 \times \quad 1 = \quad 1$$

Total: 6,039,241

The sum on the right is easy to carry out, for there is only one number in each column that enters into the addition significantly and therein lies the great utility of writing numbers to a fixed *base*, in this case, 10.

Our numbers, based upon 10, are so useful and are so firmly entrenched in modern life that it seems hard to believe that they will ever be replaced. But after all, there is nothing very special about the number 10. It merely happens to be the number of fingers that men have and undoubtedly this is the historic reason for its employment.

It is possible to devise a system very much like the decimal system which is based upon any selected number from 2 on up. Many people have thought that a system based upon 12 would be more convenient than the decimal system since 12 has more divisors than 10 (1, 2, 3, 4, 6, and 12 as opposed to 1, 2, 5, and 10). Such a system is called a *duodecimal system* and would require 12 special symbols to represent with a single mark all the numbers from 0 through 11. A good many books have been written on this topic, but the advantages that would accrue seem to be offset many times over by the difficulties of making such a shift. It is hard enough for a country such as the U.S.A. to adopt the metric systems of weights and measures for common use, let alone to institute a fundamental revolution in writing numbers.

Yet, as has been said, form frequently follows function. This means that the shape that things take is determined to some extent by the use to which they are put. An animal who must find food on the high branches must grow a long neck. So with numbers; a surprising example of this principle has developed in the last 15 years. The *binary system* of numbers has largely displaced the decimal system in the design and use of high speed computing machinery.

The *binary* system is based upon the number two. It requires only two special symbols: 0 and 1, and it is precisely this feature that makes it so very important in the construction and the use of high speed electronic computing machinery. These machines utilize electronic switches. A simple switch has two conditions: either it is on or it is off. Electronic engineers in combining these switches have found that it is possible to represent the "off condition" by a 0 and the "on condition" by a 1. All other logical and arithmetical situations can be built up by a combination of these two simple elements. The binary system is tailor made for electronic computers.

To build up the binary system, we begin by making a table of the successive products of two:

$$1 = 1$$
$$2 \times 1 = 2$$
$$2 \times 2 \times 1 = 4$$
$$2 \times 2 \times 2 \times 1 = 8$$
$$2 \times 2 \times 2 \times 2 \times 1 = 16$$

These products are the fundamental building blocks of the binary system and every number can be expressed in terms of them. For instance, since

$$29 = 16 + 8 + 4 + 1 = 2^4 + 2^3 + 2^2 + 1$$

(notice that a 2^1 is missing), the number 11101 is binary for 29. A "1" indicates that a particular fundamental quantity is present; a "0" that it is absent. Notice that

$$1 \times 16 = 16$$
$$1 \times 8 = 8$$
$$1 \times 4 = 4$$
$$0 \times 2 = 0$$
$$1 \times 1 = \underline{1}$$
$$\text{Total:} \quad 29$$

Decimal	Binary	Decimal	Binary
1	1	9	1001
2	10	10	1010
3	11	11	1011
4	100	12	1100
5	101	13	1101
6	110	14	1110
7	111	15	1111
8	1000	16	10000

Figure 5. Table of binary numbers

Complete rules can be given for doing arithmetic in the binary system and for expressing decimal numbers in binary and binary numbers in decimal. It would take us too far afield to do so, and a few examples must suffice. The addition table and the multiplication table for binaries are absurdly simple (a wonderful feature):

+	0	1
0	0	1
1	1	10

Addition table
for binary numbers

×	0	1
0	0	0
1	0	1

Multiplication table
for binary numbers

Figure 6

To multiply in the binary system 1100 (i.e., 12 in decimal) by 101 (i.e., 5 in decimal) work exactly as in decimal but use the above rules.

$$
\begin{array}{r}
1100 \\
\times\ 101 \\
\hline
1100 \\
0000 \\
1100 \\
\hline
111100
\end{array}
$$

The answer, 111100, is of course in binary, and to see what it is in ordinary numbers we must convert it:

$$
\begin{array}{rcl}
1 \times 32 &=& 32 \\
1 \times 16 &=& 16 \\
1 \times 8 &=& 8 \\
1 \times 4 &=& 4 \\
0 \times 2 &=& 0 \\
0 \times 1 &=& 0 \\
\hline
\text{Total:} && 60
\end{array}
$$

The Development of the Digits*

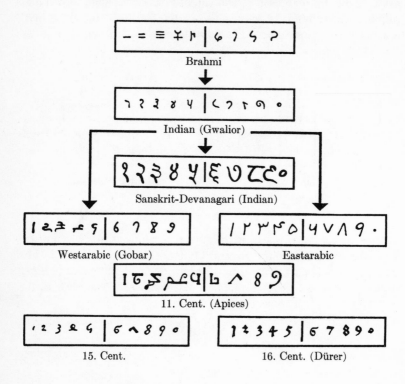

Brahmi

Indian (Gwalior)

Sanskrit-Devanagari (Indian)

Westarabic (Gobar)

Eastarabic

11. Cent. (Apices)

15. Cent.

16. Cent. (Dürer)

Contemporary

20th Century from
high speed printer

20th Century indentification numbers on
checks, suitable for high speed processing

21st Century?

Figure 7

* After van der Waerden, modified by author.

The symbols 0 and 1 when used in the binary system are known as *bits*. This is a new term in the language and was created from the syllables *binary digits*. Although every number can be written with bits, it takes far more bits than digits to represent the same number:

Sixteen = 16 (in the decimal system): two digits

Sixteen = 10000 (in the binary system): five bits.

On the average, somewhat more than three times as many bits as digits must be used. This seeming disadvantage is outweighed, as far as electronic equipment is concerned, by the great simplifications in wiring that result from the simple addition and multiplication tables.

Problem Set 4

1. How many letters must be employed to write in full the number 16,375,289,182,343,892?

2. If you know a foreign language, write out the number 72,893 in full in that language. How many letters are employed? How much saving results from using numerals?

3. How many different one digit numbers are there? How many different two digit numbers are there? What is the general rule?

4. How many two digit numbers have a zero in them? How many three digit numbers have at least one zero in them?

5. How can you tell just by looking at the digits which of two numbers is the larger? Can you formulate a rule? Try out your rule on 60,291 and 60,621.

6. A number is to be formed with the digits 1, 1, 6, 4, 4, 9, 9. What is the largest and smallest number that can be formed?

7. Do the same problem with the digits 1, 1, 0, 2, 2, 3.

8. Arrange the first twenty numbers in alphabetical order.

9. Which is larger LXXXVIII or C?

10. Multiply XXII by LXIV. Try to do this without changing the Roman numerals to ordinary numbers.

11. A table of counting reads:

one dozen = 12
one gross = 12 dozen
one great gross = 12 gross

What system of numbers does this suggest?

12. The words folio, quarto, octavo, sixteenmo, and thirty-twomo occur in the book industry. Find out what they mean and how they arise. What system of numbers do these expressions suggest?

13. A state wishes to issue about one million license plates. About how much saving of metal would occur if it used all letters instead of numbers?

14. Who was right, Abigail Adams or Thomas Jefferson? In 1787, Thomas Jefferson's younger daughter, Polly, stopped off with Abigail and John Adams in London on her way to Paris to join her father. Mrs. Adams observed that Polly had 'cloathes only proper for the sea', and so purchased some for the young girl and her maid. She sent the following bill to Jefferson:

	£	s	d
Paid for bringing the Trunks from Tower Hill		5	6
Four fine Irish Holland frocks	3	10	
5 yd. white dimity for shirts		15	
4 yd. checked muslin for a frock	1	10	
3 yd. lace Edging to trim it		6	6
To making the frock		5	
3 yd. flannel for undercoats		7	6
A Brown Bever Hat and feathers		13	
2 pr. leather Gloves		2	4
5 yd. diaper for arm cloths		5	10
6 pr. cotton Stockings		13	6
3 yd. blue sash Ribbon		3	
To diaper for pockets, linning, tape, cloth for night caps, etc.		5	6
To a comb and case, comb Brush, tooth Brush		1	6
For the Maid Servant			
12 yds. calico for 2 short Gown and Coats	1	5	6
4 yd. half Irish linen for Aprons		7	4
3 pr. Stockings		6	
2 yd. linning		2	
1 Shawl handkerchief		4	6
paid for washing		6	8
Sterling	10	15	8

Jefferson changed the total to £11/16/2.† Which sum is correct? Americans don't often get a chance to do sums in the English system. How do you like it?

15. A number written in binary ends in a 0. Show that it is an even number. A number ends in 00. What can you say about it?

† *The Adams-Jefferson Letters.* L. J. Capon, ed., Chapel Hill, 1959, vol. 1, p. 186.

5. Powers and Exponents

Large numbers are very long. It is important to look for short ways to deal with them. One of the most useful ways that has been devised is that of *powers* and *exponents*. Powers are special numbers which result when one fixed number is multiplied by itself over and over again. Thus, the *powers of two* are:

$$2 = 2$$
$$2 \times 2 = 4$$
$$2 \times 2 \times 2 = 8$$
$$2 \times 2 \times 2 \times 2 = 16$$

and so forth. The *powers of three* are:

$$3 = 3$$
$$3 \times 3 = 9$$
$$3 \times 3 \times 3 = 27$$
$$3 \times 3 \times 3 \times 3 = 81$$

and so forth. The *powers of ten* are:

$$10 = 10$$
$$10 \times 10 = 100$$
$$10 \times 10 \times 10 = 1,000$$
$$10 \times 10 \times 10 \times 10 = 10,000$$

and so forth. The number 2 itself is called the *first power of* 2, 4 $(= 2 \times 2)$ is called the *second power of* 2, 8 $(= 2 \times 2 \times 2)$ is called the *third power of* 2, and so forth. If, for instance, 2 were multiplied by itself 11 times, the resulting number would be called the *11th power of* 2. It takes a bit of space to write

$$2 \times 2 \times 2 \times 2 \times 2 \times 2 \times 2 \times 2 \times 2 \times 2 \times 2 ,$$

so mathematicians about 300 years ago devised a special shorthand notation. It is this: 2^{11}. The small number above the two is called an *exponent* and indicates that the number below it is to be multiplied by itself 11 times. (The symbols 2^{11} are read "two to the 11th" or "two to the 11th power.") The following table indicates how exponents work.

1st power	$2^1 = 2$
2nd power	$2^2 = 2 \times 2 = 4$
3rd power	$2^3 = 2 \times 2 \times 2 = 8$
4th power	$2^4 = 2 \times 2 \times 2 \times 2 = 16$
5th power	$2^5 = \quad\quad 32$
6th power	$2^6 = \quad\quad 64$
7th power	$2^7 = \quad\quad 128$
8th power	$2^8 = \quad\quad 256$
9th power	$2^9 = \quad\quad 512$
10th power	$2^{10} = \quad\quad 1{,}024$
11th power	$2^{11} = \quad\quad 2{,}048$
12th power	$2^{12} = \quad\quad 4{,}096$
13th power	$2^{13} = \quad\quad 8{,}192$
14th power	$2^{14} = \quad\quad 16{,}384$
15th power	$2^{15} = \quad\quad 32{,}768$
16th power	$2^{16} = \quad\quad 65{,}536$
17th power	$2^{17} = \quad\quad 131{,}072$
18th power	$2^{18} = \quad\quad 262{,}144$
19th power	$2^{19} = \quad\quad 524{,}288$
20th power	$2^{20} = 1{,}048{,}576$

Figure 8. The first 20 powers of 2

In dealing with exponents it is essential to distinguish their use from that of multiplication; 2^7 means $2 \times 2 \times 2 \times 2 \times 2 \times 2 \times 2 = 128$, and it must be distinguished from $2 \times 7 = 14$.

Problem Set 5

1. Compute the first 5 powers of 5.
2. Compute the first 5 powers of 1. What is the general rule?
3. Compute the first 5 powers of $1\frac{1}{2}$.
4. Compute the first 5 powers of 0. General rule?
5. Is 2^7 the same as 7^2? Is 4^3 the same as 3^4?
6. If 10^{100} were written out in full, how many symbols would it take? How many symbols are employed when exponents are used? How much saving is made?

The powers of ten are particularly important because of our use of the denary scale. Here is a table:

1st power	10^1 = 10	ten
2nd power	10^2 = 100	one hundred
3rd power	10^3 = 1,000	one thousand
4th power	10^4 = 10,000	ten thousand
5th power	10^5 = 100,000	one hundred thousand
6th power	10^6 = 1,000,000	one million
7th power	10^7 = 10,000,000	ten million
8th power	10^8 = 100,000,000	one hundred million
9th power	10^9 = 1,000,000,000	one billion
10th power	10^{10} = 10,000,000,000	ten billion
11th power	10^{11} = 100,000,000,000	one hundred billion
12th power	10^{12} = 1,000,000,000,000	one trillion
13th power	10^{13} = 10,000,000,000,000	ten trillion
14th power	10^{14} = 100,000,000,000,000	one hundred trillion

Figure 9. The first 14 powers of 10

If you examine this table, you will see that in every power of ten the number of zeros following the initial 1 is exactly equal to the exponent. This makes it very easy to give meaning to such powers. For instance, 10^{63} when written out in full would be a 1 followed by 63 zeros.

Problem Set 5 (cont.)

7. Which is larger 5^6 or 6^5?

8. What would 2^{3+5} be? What would $(3 + 5)^2$ be?

9. How many digits in the numbers 2^7, 2^{10}, 2^{14}, and 2^{17}? Can you find an approximate rule for finding out how many digits there are in 2^n?

10. Write the following number in exponent form: Ten to the one millionth power. If it were all written out, how many digits would this number have?

6. The Names of Really Large Numbers

The development of an individual, so they say, reflects in miniature the development of the species. So with numbers. A child cannot conceive large numbers and, indeed, has no need for them. The race of men over centuries has had no need for them and so has taken a long time to arrive at the higher powers of ten. The largest uncompounded number word that occurs in the original, ancient Hebrew version of the Old Testament is ten thousand (r'vavah). Numbers that were still larger were made by compounding the smaller numbers. This can be done in English also: one hundred thousand, one thousand thousand. It required almost an additional two millennia before a single word was used to express a number of this order of magnitude. The word was *million*. It was an Italian invention of the 13th century, and means, simply, "a large thousand." By combination, still larger numbers were made: ten million, one hundred million. The word *billion* had to wait till the beginning of the 17th century to be adopted in English, and then it was more of a curiosity than anything else. It really took the 20th century with the large numbers occurring in science and economics to put billions on the map.

What comes after billions? This is a question that people frequently ask. If they happen to know the answer, trillions, then the question may well become, what comes after trillions? Let us see about these questions in a general sort of way. Certain powers of ten have special words attached to them. The first few of these are

$$10^1 = \text{ten}$$
$$10^2 = \text{hundred}$$
$$10^3 = \text{thousand}$$
$$10^6 = \text{million}$$
$$10^9 = \text{billion}$$
$$10^{12} = \text{trillion}$$

and so on. It is the "so on" that we must talk about. After an irregular start in which the first three powers of 10 are singled out for special designations, every third power thereafter receives a special name. The powers between 10^3 and 10^6, between 10^6 and 10^9, between 10^9 and 10^{12}, etc. do not have special one word names, but are called successively "ten" or "a hundred" followed by the next lowest name in the special list of names. For instance:

$$10^{10} = ten \text{ billion (billion} = 10^9)$$
$$10^{11} = one\ hundred \text{ billion}$$

then,

$$10^{12} = one \text{ trillion}$$
$$10^{13} = ten \text{ trillion}$$
$$10^{14} = one\ hundred \text{ trillion.}$$

This is the system that is used in the U.S.A. In order to go beyond, we need special names for the powers 10^{15}, 10^{18}, etc. Here they are, at least as far as Webster's *Unabridged Dictionary* lists them:

Power	Number word	Latin root	Numerical equivalent of root
10^9	billion	bi-	2
10^{12}	trillion	tri-	3
10^{15}	quadrillion	quater	4
10^{18}	quintillion	quintus	5
10^{21}	sextillion	sex	6
10^{24}	septillion	septem	7
10^{27}	octillion	octo	8
10^{30}	nonillion	novem	9
10^{33}	decillion	decem	10
10^{36}	undecillion	undecim	11
10^{39}	duodecillion	duodecim	12
10^{42}	tredecillion	tredecim	13
10^{45}	quattuordecillion	quattuordecim	14
10^{48}	quindecillion	quindecim	15
10^{51}	sexdecillion	sexdecim	16
10^{54}	septendecillion	septendecim	17
10^{57}	octodecillion	octodecim	18
10^{60}	novemdecillion	novemdecim	19
10^{63}	vigintillion	viginti	20

Figure 10. Table of the special powers of 10 possessing simple names

Some of these "illions" are familiar, but probably not all. Starting with billions, the prefixes come from Latin words which refer to the numbers 2, 3, 4, . . . , 20. What is the relation between the power of 10 and the number that acts as a prefix to "illion"? If you examine the last table carefully, you will come to the following conclusion:

Multiply by 3 *the number indicated by the Latin prefix. Then add* 3 *to the product. The result will be the proper power of* 10. *Thus,*

$$\text{trillion} = 10^{12}; \quad (3 \times 3) + 3 = 12$$
$$\text{quadrillion} = 10^{15}; \quad (3 \times 4) + 3 = 15$$
$$\text{vigintillion} = 10^{63}; \quad (3 \times 20) + 3 = 63.$$

We are now in a position to give names to very large numbers. Take 30293748092801008156 as an example. We proceed as follows: The first thing to do is to separate the number into groups of three digits each starting from the right-hand end. This yields

$$30,293,748,092,801,008,156.$$

Now (counting from the right) we associate with each group of three digits one of the special number names.

With the first group we associate units.

With the second group we associate thousands.

With the third group we associate millions.

With the fourth group we associate billions.

With the fifth group we associate trillions.

With the sixth group we associate quadrillions.

With the seventh group we associate quintillions.

If there were more groups we would merely go down the list given in Figure 10. The number can now be read. It is: 30 quintillion, 293 quadrillion, 748 trillion, 92 billion, 801 million, 8 thousand, 156.

Why does the dictionary stop with vigintillions? Well, it had to stop somewhere, and one vigintillion (10^{63}) seems to be sufficiently large to deal with any number that may arise in a popular or scientific context and which must be named compactly in books or newspapers. Furthermore, carrying these "illions" beyond one vigintillion according to the rule just mentioned which employs Latin prefixes leads to language difficulties and to inelegant expressions. The Latin word for 21 is viginti et unus.

With these special names as provided to us by the dictionary, we are able to give a name to every number from 1 to $10^{66} - 1$. Beyond this, the dictionary is silent. You are at liberty, therefore, to invent your own names! And people have invented some strange ones indeed. For instance, Kasner and Newman in their delightful *Mathematics and the Imagination*, introduce the names:

$$10^{100} = \text{one googol}$$

$$10^{\text{googol}} = 10^{10^{100}} = \text{one googolplex.}$$

But these outlandish names are by no means standard. Truth to tell, the lack of names is not very serious. Scientists, who are about the only people who need extraordinarily large numbers, write them in their decimal or exponential forms, and do not refer to them by their proper names. Thus, the number written 10^{63} would be referred to as "ten to the 63" and hardly ever by the dictionary term "one vigintillion."

Figure 11. One vigintillion

There are other terms which are employed by scientists when referring to large multiples of physical quantities. These arise when the metric systems of measurement are employed. Everybody has probably heard the expression *kilo*cycles and *mega*cycles in connection with radio transmission. A cycle is one vibration. A kilocycle is one thousand = 10^3 vibrations. A megacycle is one million = 10^6 vibrations. When people deal with these quantities on a day to day basis it is more convenient to say, for instance, a megacycle than "a million cycles" or "ten to the sixth cycles." Since scientists have pushed to incredible limits the boundaries of measurement and since until recently no prefixes beyond mega existed, new prefixes had to be constructed and adopted. In the fall of 1958, an international committee on weights and measures met in Paris and, among other things, adopted as standard the following prefixes for very large multiples:

Multiples	Prefix	Abbreviation
$1\ 000\ 000\ 000\ 000\ =\ 10^{12}$	tera	T
$1\ 000\ 000\ 000\ =\ 10^{9}$	giga	G
$1\ 000\ 000\ =\ 10^{6}$	mega	M
$1\ 000\ =\ 10^{3}$	kilo	k
$100\ =\ 10^{2}$	hecto	h
$10\ =\ 10$	deka	dk

Figure 12. Standard prefixes for large multiples

Problem Set 6

1. The number of "working parts" in a human body has been estimated at ten thousand million. Express this as a power.

2. Which is larger: a million billion or a billion million? Express these in another way.

3. If the Latin root for one hundred is *cent*, what, according to our rule would a centillion be?

4. The digits of $10^{66} - 1$ are written out in full. Describe the number.

5. The digits of $10^{20} + 10^{10} + 1$ are written out in full. Describe them.

6. It is desired to arrange the names of *all* the numbers in alphabetical order. Explain some of the difficulties that you would run into with this project.

7. Read the number: 12,345,678,900,000,000.

8. Write the number: Six and one-half sextillion.

7. The Law of Exponents

This is a fundamental law of mathematics and tells us that numbers expressed as powers of the same base can be multiplied by the simpler process of adding their exponents. Suppose we would like to obtain 16×128. We can, of course, multiply it out and obtain

$$16 \times 128 = 2048 .$$

But suppose we have noticed that

$$16 = 2^4 = 2 \times 2 \times 2 \times 2 \text{ (four 2's multiplied together)}$$

and $\quad 128 = 2^7 = 2 \times 2 \times 2 \times 2 \times 2 \times 2 \times 2$

(seven 2's multiplied together).

Then,

four 2's $\qquad\qquad\qquad$ seven 2's

$$2^4 \times 2^7 = (2 \times 2 \times 2 \times 2) \times (2 \times 2 \times 2 \times 2 \times 2 \times 2 \times 2) \,.$$

The net result is 11 2's multiplied together. This is a number which can be represented as 2^{11}. Thus,

$$16 \times 128 = 2^4 \times 2^7 = 2^{4+7} = 2^{11} = 2048 \,.$$

The same is true for any exponents whatever,

$$2^m \times 2^n = 2^{m+n},$$

and is also true if the 2's are replaced by any other number whatever. Here we have the *first law of exponents*

$$a^m \times a^n = a^{m+n} \,.$$

This contains within it the germ of *logarithms*, a device which permits multiplication to be carried out by means of addition.

Now we know that $a^m \times a^n = a^{m+n}$. In particular

$$a^m \times a^m = a^{m+m} = a^{2m} \,.$$

But $a^m \times a^m$ means "a^m multiplied by itself" and this is a process that is symbolized by the exponent 2. That is,

$$a^m \times a^m = [a^m]^2 \,.$$

This shows that

$$[a^m]^2 = a^{2m} \,.$$

Similarly, by the law of exponents,

$$a^m \times a^m \times a^m = a^m \times a^{m+m}$$
$$= a^m \times a^{2m}$$
$$= a^{m+2m}$$
$$= a^{3m} \,.$$

And so

$$[a^m]^3 = a^{3m} \,.$$

What is happening here must be obvious. If n is any number, we have

$$[a^m]^n = a^{mn}.$$

This is the *second law of exponents*. It enables the powering of powers to be reduced to multiplication.

Problem Set 7

1. Find (a) $6^8 \times 6^{10}$ (c) $(6^8)^3$
   (b) $6^8 \times 6^8$ (d) $2^4 \times 4^2$

   Leave the answers in exponential form.

2. Which is larger: 10^{100} or 100^{10}? 8^{16} or 16^8?

3. Is $(2 + 5)^4 = 2^4 + 5^4$?

4. Is $(1 + 2 + 3)^4 = 1^4 + 2^4 + 3^4$?

5. Establish the rule: $a^m \times a^n \times a^p = a^{m+n+p}$

6. Establish the rule: $(ab)^m = a^m \times b^m$

7. Establish the rule: $[(a^m)^m]^m = a^{(m^3)}$

8. *Two stage exponents*: We may put exponents on exponents, for instance 7^{2^2}. By this will be meant 7 to the 2^2 power. That is, $7^4 = 2401$. Compute 2^{2^2}, 2^{2^3}, 3^{2^2}. The symbol a^{bc} is always taken to mean $a^{(bc)}$ because the other apparent possibility, $(a^b)^c$, is simply a^{bc}.

9. Is there a difference between: $3^{(2^3)}$ and $(3^2)^3$?

10. *Three stage exponents*: Determine: $2^{2^{2^2}}$. (We mean 2 raised to the 2^{2^2} power.)

8. Scientific Notation

Numbers such as $100 = 10^2$ or $1000 = 10^3$ are easy to write as powers. What shall we do with a number such as 200? There are two things that can be done. The first is simple, the second more difficult. The first leads to a mode of expression which is commonly employed in science and in other places where large numbers are encountered. The second leads to logarithms.

Notice that

$$200 = 2 \times 100 = 2 \times 10^2$$
$$273 = 2.73 \times 100 = 2.73 \times 10^2$$
$$2,736 = 2.736 \times 1,000 = 2.736 \times 10^3$$
$$52,810 = 5.281 \times 10,000 = 5.281 \times 10^4$$
$$173,924 = 1.73924 \times 100,000 = 1.73924 \times 10^5$$

From these examples we conclude that *every number can be written as a decimal which lies between* 1 *and* 10 *multiplied by* 10 *raised to an appropriate power.* Let us agree that this will constitute a standard form for writing numbers. We shall call this form the *scientific form.*

Since 2,736 takes 5 symbols (including the comma) to write and 2.736 × 10³ takes 9 symbols (including the decimal point) one may legitimately wonder why this type of notation should be employed. Again, form follows function. The answer lies in the ease with which approximate computations can be carried out when numbers have been expressed in this manner. The law of exponents comes to our aid and helps us keep track of the decimal point. These matters will be explained in the section on approximate computation.

A	A*	
0.65296969E − 05	−0.10335573E	07
−0.23549674E − 05	−0.90385066E	05
−0.14027680E 03	−0.19387733E	04
−0.68200212E − 02	−0.92296533E	03
0.96533915E 08	0.96533810E	08
0.61061934E − 09	−0.78643200E	01
0.14612067E 08	0.14612064E	08
0.48001909E − 00	0.40413866E −	00
−0.25227512E − 00	−0.26034176E −	00

Figure 13. "Floating numbers." Computing machine
answers are frequently in scientific form

A modified scientific form of writing numbers is frequently employed in electronic computers. In the above list, taken from an actual computation, the letter E (for "exponent") splits each number into two portions. The first is called the *mantissa* and the second the *characteristic*. The characteristic indicates the power of ten and the 10 itself is omitted. The number −0.10335573E 07 must be interpreted as −0.10335573 × 10⁷ = −1033557.3. The number 0.65296969E − 05 is 0.65296969 × 10⁻⁵ = .0000065296969. (See Section 13.) Here every mantissa is written as a decimal between 0 and 1.)

Problem Set 8

1. Express the following numbers in scientific form:
   (a) 365,   (b) 10,078,   (c) 6,329,480.
2. Express the following numbers in scientific notation:
   (a) two billion, five hundred million,
   (b) six and one-half trillion.

9. How Large Is Large?

One of the strange things about large numbers is our inability to visualize their size or to comprehend their enormity. There is a good reason for this. We know the small numbers fairly well because we deal with them frequently. Our family may consist of 4 or 5 members. We can visualize an egg box with 12 pockets for eggs. We have handled a roll of pennies with 50 pennies in it. We have flipped a book with several hundred pages. When it comes to the thousands, it is somewhat harder to find examples. In our day to day living, we rarely encounter and deal with groups of thousands of things. Higher numbers are even more rare and our feeling for them is correspondingly more vague. If large numbers intrude, we very frequently avoid them by introducing a larger unit which has the effect of producing small numbers once again. The housewife deals with *one* dozen of eggs and not *twelve* eggs. The astronomer prefers to deal with a small number of *light years* rather than an enormous number of *miles*.

Nor do really large numbers of things present themselves to our visual consciousness. If we are lucky enough to attend a Rose Bowl game, we may "see" 100,000 people at one time. But no one has ever seen ten million people simultaneously. Nor if the Rose Bowl had exactly 100,000 spectators at a certain game could we visually comprehend the 100,000 as a precise quantity. A few thousand people more or less, added or subtracted from the stands, would hardly make a perceptible difference to us. In other words, except for very low numbers, we cannot count by mere looking.

How, then, can we obtain an appreciation of the size of large numbers? We can do it to a certain extent by thinking about them in a way which relates them to human activity and to smaller numbers which are within comprehension.

How large is a million (10^6)? Suppose we answer this by imagining that we have a large grandfather clock whose pendulum swings once a second producing a "tick" and a "tock," two sounds in all. How long shall we have to wait for one million sounds? At the rate of

2 a second there will be $2 \times 60 = 120$ a minute. There will be $120 \times 60 = 7,200$ in an hour. In a day, assuming that one can listen to them, there will be $7,200 \times 24 = 172,800$. In 6 days there will be 1,036,800 ticks and tocks. Almost 6 days to tick away one million!

Take the telephone book of a large city. The one I have before me has pages of four columns $12''$ long and an average of about 100 phones per column. That is 400 names per page. There are 1347 pages. This yields about 538,800 names, over a half-million. If I consider first names and second names as separate then I can have in my hand over a million names. Strangely, to me at least, the number of ticks and tocks in 6 days seems far less than the number of names in a fat telephone book. But there is the figure. At any rate, it is not too difficult to get to a million (10^6) objects. With ten phone books we can get to ten million (10^7) objects. In fact, one might even contemplate the large trucks that deliver these books. Perhaps there were one thousand such books loaded on a truck when it left the warehouse. This would yield $10^9 =$ one billion names. One might even contemplate the entire edition of this particular phone book. It must be at least 500,000 — one for each subscriber— and this would mean $500,000 \times 1,000,000$ names $= 5 \times 10^{11}$ names. Five hundred billion names printed. Here the imagination begins to falter. For while we can think of scanning the names in a single phone book as a possible activity, the thought of scanning a half-million such books is out of the question.

Let us begin again. A beach is a familiar thing and so is a grain of sand. A grain may be an insignificant thing in a child's pail, but not so when it wreaks havoc with the insides of an expensive camera. Let us compute the number of grains of sand on the beach. For the sake of the argument, suppose that the beach is 1 mile long, 100 feet wide and 1 foot deep. Suppose further that a grain of sand is a small cube $\frac{1}{100}$ of an inch on each side. Then it is not too difficult to show that the number of grains will be around 10^{14}, i.e., one hundred trillion. If we contemplated a thousand or ten thousand such beaches, the number of grains would go up to $10^{18} =$ one *quintillion*. But while we may, so to speak, "grasp" the number on one beach, the number on one thousand beaches, or on the whole Sahara, is beyond "grasping."

The truth, then, seems to be this. Thousands, though uncommon, are familiar enough things. Millions can even be visualized in terms of everyday things. Perhaps even billions, trillions, and quadrillions.

When we reach quintillions (10^{18}) we are dealing with really large numbers. We enter the realm where numbers lose all significance in relation to human activities and become the pure creation of mathematics to be treated by the methods of mathematics.

10. Approximate Numbers and Orders of Magnitude

If a man is poor and has only a dollar in his jeans another dollar may be of vital importance to him. But if a man is a millionaire another dollar would concern him little. It would take another million to make him sit up and take notice. There is a general principle at work here. In many situations we are interested in numbers only on a percentage basis. This means that if a number is small, we would like to know it down to the last unit, but if it is very large, we may only need to know it approximately. Inaccuracy may also be forced upon us. There are many times when we must content ourselves with approximate answers to questions, for exact answers may be impossible to obtain. The distance from the earth to the nearest star outside the solar system is such a number. In this way the notion of approximate numbers and approximate computation arises, sometimes by choice, sometimes by necessity.

Approximate computation is inexact computation with numbers that have been expressed roughly. If a number is given exactly, it may be *rounded* and expressed approximately. The process is carried out as follows:

A 5 digit number given exactly:	$37,287 = 3.7287 \times 10^4$
The number rounded to 4 significant figures:	$37,290 = 3.729 \times 10^4$
The number rounded to 3 significant figures:	$37,300 = 3.73 \times 10^4$
The number rounded to 2 significant figures:	$37,000 = 3.7 \times 10^4$
The number rounded to 1 significant figure:	$40,000 = 4 \times 10^4$

Figure 14. The rounding of numbers

Working backwards, we can say that we are dealing with a number which is 40,000, *to the nearest ten thousand.* A little more accurately, it is 37,000, *to the nearest thousand.* More accurately still, it is 37,300, *to the nearest hundred.* And so on. In rounding, then, we replace the last two digits by the nearest multiple of 10, or the last three digits by the nearest multiple of 100, and so forth. If the digits to be rounded stand halfway between two multiples, as is the case with 37,285, we could "round up" to 37,290 or "round down" to 37,280. The choice is the computer's.

Sometimes equations must be written with approximate numbers. If one writes $37,287 = 3.73 \times 10^4$, this is not an exact equation but only an approximate one. Though the error committed is, relatively speaking, very small, we should be aware of it. The special symbol $\approx$ is used for approximate equalities, and this helps avoid difficulties. Thus, it is better to write $37,287 \approx 3.73 \times 10^4$.

The *order of magnitude* of a number is the number which results when the given number has been rounded to one significant figure. Here are some examples:

Exact value	Rounded to 1 significant figure	Order of magnitude
255	300	3×10^2
37,287	40,000	4×10^4
655,409	700,000	7×10^5

Problem Set 10

1. Round the number 372,945 to 5 significant figures; to four figures, to three figures, to one figure.

2. Round the number 302,000 to one figure.

3. Why do you suppose that the process described in this section is called "rounding"?

4. An atlas lists the 1950 population of New York City as 7,891,957. Do you think that the number of inhabitants of such a large city can be determined exactly? What do you suppose this exact figure represents?

5. An atlas lists the population of Persia as 19,000,000. What can you say about this number?

6. The land and water area of the United States is listed as 3,022,387 square miles. What is the order of magnitude of this number?

7. Interpret and verify the following statements:
   (a) $2^{15} \approx 3.28 \times 10^4$,
   (b) The number of cubic inches in a cubic yard $\approx 4.67 \times 10^4$.

11. Approximate Computation

Exact computation is frequently difficult and tedious to carry out. It is important to learn and to get into the habit of doing approximate computations. Not only is it a time saver, but the approximate answers can serve as a guide if exact answers are required and can help catch gross blunders. Here is the way in which it is done.

(a) *Addition.* Round all the numbers and add the resulting numbers.

EXAMPLE:

Exact	One Digit Rounded (nearest 10's)
374,921	374,920
8,255	8,260
297	300
383,473	383,480

Two Digits Rounded (nearest 100's)	Three Digits Rounded (nearest 1000's)
374,900	375,000
8,300	8,000
300	000
383,500	383,000

Four Digits Rounded (nearest 10,000's)
370,000
10,000
000
380,000

(b) *Subtraction.* Proceed as with addition. But a word of caution is necessary. The more the numbers differ, the more rounding you may do. If the numbers are close together, you may not be able to round without significantly destroying the value of the whole computation.

First Example:

Exact	One Digit Rounded
839,403	839,400
− 1,018	− 1,020
838,385	838,380

Two Digits Rounded	Three Digits Rounded
839,400	839,000
− 1,000	− 1,000
838,400	838,000

Second Example:

Exact	One Digit Rounded
839,403	839,400
−839,287	−839,290
116	110

Two Digits Rounded	Three Digits Rounded
839,400	839,000
−839,300	−839,000
100	0

The last answer may be of no value at all.

(c) *Multiplication.* Here it is convenient to use scientific notation. Round the multiplier and multiplicand down to the same number of significant figures. Express in scientific notation and multiply using the law of exponents for the powers of 10. You may need to round once again after multiplication.

Example:

Exact	Rounded to 2 Figures	Rounded to 1 Figure
7583	7.6×10^3	8×10^3
$\times$ 24	2.4×10	2×10
30332	304	16×10^4
15166	152	
181992	18.24×10^4	
	$1.8\ \ \times 10^5$	2×10^5

(d) *Division.*   Round the dividend and divisor down to the same number of significant figures, and express in scientific notation. Divide and use the law of exponents as explained in Section 7 to handle the powers of 10.   Round once again after division.

EXAMPLE: $75839 \div 246$

<u>Exact</u>

$$308.2886 = 3.082886 \times 10^2$$

$$
\begin{array}{r}
246 \,\overline{)75839.0000} \\
\underline{738} \\
2039 \\
\underline{1968} \\
710 \\
\underline{492} \\
2180 \\
\underline{1968} \\
2120 \\
\underline{1968} \\
1520 \\
\underline{1476} \\
44 \text{ remainder}
\end{array}
$$

<u>Rounded to Two Significant Figures</u>

$$(7.6 \times 10^4) \div (2.5 \times 10^2) \approx 3.0 \times 10^2$$

$$
\begin{array}{r}
3.04 \\
2.5 \,\overline{)7.600} \\
\underline{7\,5} \\
100 \\
\underline{100} \\
000
\end{array}
$$

<u>Rounded to One Significant Figure</u>

$$(8 \times 10^4) \div (2 \times 10^2) = 4 \times 10^2$$

Since division is such an unpleasant process, rounding to one figure is advised if low accuracy is sufficient. A small slide rule is quite useful for doing approximate multiplications and divisions.

Problem Set 11

1. Compute approximately:
    (a) $\$1.79 + \$10.82 + \$0.03 + \$9.22$
    (b) $68 \times 91 \times 43$
2. Compute approximately the number of inches in a mile.

3. Compute approximately the number of square feet in an acre.

4. Compute approximately the number of square inches in a circle of radius 10 feet.

5. A large globe in a public library has a diameter of 3 feet. Compute approximately the number of cubic inches in its volume.

6. Approximately how many Sundays have there been since 500 B.C.?

7. How accurately do banks carry out their computations?

8. The sun moves about 26 miles per second in space. Compute approximately how many miles it travels in a year.

9. Compute approximately the number of square miles on the surface of the earth.

10. *The Klondike Bubble.*   Several years ago one of the popular breakfast foods carried an offer on the back of its box to sell one square inch of land in the Klondike for $.25. Payment of the quarter entitled you to a deed which described your property and for a small additional charge, the company would supply you with a small bag of dirt from the general vicinity. Compute the gross income per acre. Estimate the profit per acre.

11. *Rounding the Income Tax.*   According to the instructions on a recent federal income tax form, "money items on your return . . . may be shown as whole dollar amounts. This means that you may eliminate any amount less than 50 cents and increase any amount from 50 cents through 99 cents to the next higher dollar." What is the point of this?

12. There are no coins that are as small as $\frac{1}{10}\cancel{c}$. Why, then, is the price of gasoline at filling stations quoted to $\frac{1}{10}\cancel{c}$?

12. The Rough Art of Estimation

Some newspapers are in the habit of printing odd bits of information as crack fillers. This material very often involves large numbers. You have probably seen them: the annual production of Christmas tree light bulbs, the number of ponds in Saskatchewan, the annual consumption of hot dogs, the number of railway ties in North America, the rat population of New York City, etc., etc. Amusing in themselves, these estimates frequently leave the reader saying to himself, "I never thought it would be so large a number" and "How on earth do they know what the number is?"

Assuming that the number is not one which was pulled out of thin air, there are two ways "they" can know. First way: An actual record of the quantity may be available for one reason or another. Cigarettes are taxed and a record of the cigarette taxes paid—which the Treasury

Department undoubtedly has—will yield information on the number of cigarettes sold. Second way: No direct information is available, but the quantity is estimated by a series of shrewd computations based upon informed and uninformed guesses. A chain is formed which connects the desired quantity with intermediate quantities which are more easily estimated.

We shall illustrate this process by estimating the annual consumption of hot dogs in the U.S.A. One might proceed as follows: Looking at a certain person (one's own self, for instance) one observes that he makes one meal a week of hot dogs and he eats two of them. This amounts to $2 \times 52 = 104 = 1.04 \times 10^2$ hot dogs per year. Now, assume that this person is typical. Estimating the population of the U.S.A. at 1.8×10^8 individuals, we end up with an estimate of $(1.04 \times 10^2) \times (1.8 \times 10^8) \approx 1.9 \times 10^{10} = 19$ billion hot dogs per year. Note the link in the chain of reasoning: from one's self to the whole country, from the whole country to the final estimate. The first link, that one's own consumption of hot dogs is typical, may be weak. What if one hates hot dogs and never eats them? What if one loves them and eats them every day? The second estimate, that of the population of the country, is a strong one. We know that the Bureau of the Census keeps careful track of this quantity. The final answer is as good as could be obtained with the information available.

Another aspect of estimation can be illustrated by this example. While a good estimate of a quantity may be hard to come by, it may be possible to obtain an upper bound which, almost surely, will not be exceeded. It is simply not true that each individual in the country eats hot dogs morning, noon, and night, 365 days a year. If we therefore estimate this quantity for the country, it will yield a figure which will not be exceeded. Six hot dogs per day for 365 days is $6 \times 365 = 2190 \approx 2.2 \times 10^3$ hot dogs per year per individual. Multiplying this by the population we obtain

$$(2.2 \times 10^3) \times (1.8 \times 10^8) \approx 4 \times 10^{11}$$

hot dogs per year. We can swear that the annual consumption will not exceed this figure. The problem of obtaining a significant lower bound is hard here, and indeed, may be hard in many problems in mathematics. The gap between the quantity estimated and the upper bound estimated comes to a factor of about 20. The reader may feel that the first figure we computed is surely the more plausible one.

Once we have obtained this figure, and are willing to go out on a limb with it, links in a longer chain leading to additional conclusions can be set up. If we can estimate the average length of the hot dogs, we can figure up such statements as "if all the hot dogs that are eaten in one year in the U.S.A. were laid end to end, they would extend from New York City to . . . ."

There is a game called "Estimation." The object is to think of curious magnitudes and to estimate them. You win if you can estimate the quantity to within a factor of ten. There are a number of problems to play with at the end of this section. To forge the proper links may take a bit of thought, and to find the proper linking estimates may take a bit of research. No rules can be prescribed. The correct answers may not even be known.

Hot dogs and games aside, the process of estimation is an important one and must be cultivated. An estimate of seasonal unemployment may affect government policy. A good estimate of the age of a rock or the distance of a far galaxy may affect a picture of the universe. Estimation as it occurs in science has features in common with what we have just done. The links are the facts of nature which have been observed and bound together by a theory. Such a theory may involve considerable mathematics and ultimately computing. The estimate may involve experimentation, measurement, theorizing, guess work, and computation all rolled together. In order to achieve the consistency which science demands it may be important to make estimates in several totally different ways. If the answers are approximately the same, these demands are satisfied.

How old is the moon? About a century ago the astronomer Sir George Darwin formed a chain of reasoning which he believed would give an approximate answer to this question. By one series of measurements and deductions, it was found that the moon recedes from the earth 5 inches per year. By another series of measurements, the moon is now 239,000 miles away. Conclusion from these two facts: $4 \times 10^9 = 4$ billion years ago, the moon was in contact with the earth. According to the theory that the moon is a child of the earth, and formed from it, this must have been its birthday.

Problem Set 12

1. Estimate the annual consumption of ice cream in the U.S.A.

2. Estimate the number of leaves on a tree.

3. Estimate the number of snow flakes in a blizzard.

4. *Full of Beans.* A hardware store displays a gallon jug full of pea beans. The person guessing the closest to the actual number wins a bicycle. Put in an estimate.

5. Estimate the number of words defined in a large English dictionary.

6. Estimate how many Smiths there are in the U.S.A.

7. Estimate the number of different surnames in the U.S.A.

8. Estimate the number of letters in the English bible.

9. *The Chef Hofmeester's Order.* The Nieuw Amsterdam is a Dutch luxury liner that plies between Rotterdam, Holland and Hoboken, New Jersey. It makes this trip in eight days carrying a crew of 741 and 1249 passengers. Estimate how much meat the chief steward must order for a round trip to feed passengers and crew.

10. *Archimedes' Boast.* "Give me a place to stand, and I will move the earth." This is what the famous Greek scientist Archimedes (287–212 B.C.) was supposed to have said after discovering and formulating the law of the lever. Assuming that Archimedes can push with a force of 100 lbs. and that the fulcrum of the lever is 4,000 miles from the earth (see figure), estimate how far from the fulcrum he would have to stand. How far would he have to travel in order to move the earth one inch? You will need to find out what the law of the lever is.

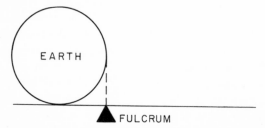

11. *Gargantuan Numbers.* One of the most famous giants in literature is Gargantua, the creation of the French satirist François Rabelais (1494–1553). As an infant, Gargantua needed 17,913 cows to supply him with milk. When, as a young man, he went to Paris to finish his education he rode on a mare that was as large as 6 elephants. He hung the bells of Notre Dame on his mare's neck as jingles. On his way home he was shot at with cannons from a castle and combed the balls from his hair with a rake 900 feet long. When he wanted to eat a salad, he cut lettuces as large as walnut trees and ate up six pilgrims who had hidden themselves among them. Assuming that as a babe and as a man, Gargantua was a certain number of times larger than his human counterparts, determine whether the figures of the cows and of the rake are consistent.

12. Without pausing to figure it out, estimate how many squares are in the grid of Fig. 15. Now compute the answer. Estimate or compute the number of squares of all sizes that can be drawn on the grid.

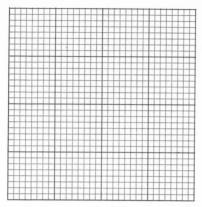

Figure 15. How many squares are here?

13. Small Numbers

We have been talking about thousands and millions and billions. These are large numbers. Compared to them, the numbers 8 or 25 are surely small. But in this section and in Section 15, we shall mean something quite different by a "small number." We shall mean a number that is *between zero and one*. Consider the fractions $\frac{1}{2}$, $\frac{2}{7}$, $\frac{4}{25}$, etc. These are all less than one and are examples of the type of number meant. The reciprocal of an integer greater than 1 is a small number. Any integer divided by a higher integer results in a number which is less than 1, and hence is a small number.

What happens when small numbers are expressed as decimals? Let us try a few:

$$\frac{98}{103} = 0.951456310\ldots$$

$$\frac{19}{59} = 0.322033898\ldots$$

$$\frac{3}{307} = 0.009771986\ldots$$

$$\frac{3}{10{,}043} = 0.000298715\ldots$$

$$\frac{21}{10{,}327{,}984} = 0.000002033\ldots$$

It appears that there is always a 0 to the left of the decimal point. There is sometimes a 0 or a string of 0's immediately to the right of the decimal point. The more zeros there are, the smaller the number is. For very small numbers, there may be many zeros, and this is inconvenient. A scientific notation for small numbers is also desirable. It is accomplished by introducing abbreviations for fundamental small quantities. These are known as *negative powers of* 10 and are written in the following way:

Fractional notation	Decimal notation	Power notation
$\dfrac{1}{10}$	.1	10^{-1}
$\dfrac{1}{100}$	.01	10^{-2}
$\dfrac{1}{1,000}$	.001	10^{-3}
$\dfrac{1}{10,000}$	.0001	10^{-4}
$\dfrac{1}{100,000}$	.00001	10^{-5}

Figure 16. Table of negative powers of 10

It is sufficient, at the beginning, to think of negative exponents as mere abbreviations. Once these fundamental symbols are available, we can write small numbers in a standard scientific form. The sample equations below indicate how it is done.

$$.2846 = \frac{2846}{10,000} = \frac{2.846}{10} = 2.846 \times \frac{1}{10} = 2.846 \times 10^{-1}$$

$$.00602 = \frac{602}{100,000} = \frac{6.02}{1,000} = 6.02 \times \frac{1}{1,000} = 6.02 \times 10^{-3}$$

$$.00000052 = \frac{52}{100,000,000} = \frac{5.2}{10,000,000}$$

$$= 5.2 \times \frac{1}{10,000,000} = 5.2 \times 10^{-7}.$$

The rule for converting a decimal between 0 and 1 into scientific notation is this: *Take the decimal and move the decimal point into the*

*standard position (i.e., immediately following the first non-zero digit).
Multiply this by* 10 *raised to the negative of a certain number. That
certain number is one more than the number of zeros between the decimal
point and the first non-zero digit of the original number.*

EXAMPLE: .00602. Non-zero part in standard position, 6.02. Number of
zeros before the 6, 2. $2 + 1 = 3$.
ANSWER: 6.02×10^{-3}.

It is desirable to have single words to designate certain small multiples of physical quantities. We have all heard of a *centi*meter which
is $\frac{1}{100} = 10^{-2}$ meter and a *milli*meter which is $\frac{1}{1000} = 10^{-3}$ meter
Here is the full list of prefixes which have been agreed upon inter-
nationally:

Verbal	Fractional	Decimal	Exp.	Prefix	Abbre-viation
one-tenth	$\frac{1}{10}$	0.1	10^{-1}	deci	d
one-hundreth	$\frac{1}{100}$	0.01	10^{-2}	centi	c
one-thousandth	$\frac{1}{1,000}$	0.001	10^{-3}	milli	m
one-millionth	$\frac{1}{1,000,000}$	0.000 001	10^{-6}	micro	μ
one-billionth	$\frac{1}{1,000,000,000}$	0.000 000 001	10^{-9}	nano	n
one-trillionth	$\frac{1}{1,000,000,000,000}$	0.000 000 000 001	10^{-12}	pico	p

Figure 17. Standard prefixes for small multiples

Problem Set 13

1. Write in scientific notation: .0040082, .00000002223.
2. Express as a decimal: 2.29×10^{-8}, 3.0077×10^{-5}.
3. How many picograms in a centigram?
4. Which is larger: $\frac{3}{127}$ or $\frac{4}{169}$?
5. Do the above problem without converting to decimals and develop a general method for answering this kind of question.

6. A carpenter has on his work bench drill bits whose diameters are: $\frac{7}{64}''$, $\frac{1}{8}''$, $\frac{5}{32}''$, $\frac{1}{4}''$, $\frac{11}{64}''$, $\frac{3}{16}''$. Arrange them in order of increasing size.

7. Given the sum: $\frac{1}{2^5} + \frac{1}{2^6} + \frac{1}{2^7} + \frac{1}{2^8} + \frac{1}{2^9} + \frac{1}{3^0}$,
   (a) estimate its size;
   (b) obtain the exact fractional answer.

14. Why Negative Exponents?

If we think back, we will recall that the positive exponents (or powers) were introduced as an abbreviation for a process of repeated multiplication. For instance, 10^5 means 10 multiplied by itself 5 times. We cannot interpret 10^{-5} in this way, for it does not make sense to say that 10^{-5} ($\frac{1}{100,000}$) is a quantity which results from writing down 10 -5 times and multiplying together. We could no more write down 10 -5 times than could a baseball pitcher make -5 consecutive strike outs. We have given a definition of the negative powers of ten as a mere abbreviation, but we can justify the wisdom of these abbreviations by relating them to the positive powers. The link that joins them is the *law of exponents* (see Section 7).

First of all, it is convenient to invent a *zeroth power* of 10: 10^0. We seek a meaning for such a thing which will be consistent with the law of exponents. If we write $10^2 \times 10^0$ and assume that the law of exponents holds for these quantities then we have

$$10^2 \times 10^0 = 10^{2+0} = 10^2 .$$

Dividing both sides of the equation by 10^2 we obtain $10^0 = 1$. We obtain the same answer, 1, no matter what power of 10 we take instead of 10^2 or no matter what number we use instead of 10. Let us therefore agree to write

$$10^0 = 1 .$$

We shall not attempt to interpret this symbol as "ten multiplied by itself zero times." The above interpretation of 10^0 comes from allowing the law of exponents to breathe life into it.

It is now possible to show that the definition of negative powers of 10 makes the law of exponents work whether the exponents are positive, negative or zero. For instance, take $10^3 \times 10^{-2}$. By the law of exponents this should be

$$10^{3-2} = 10^1 = 10 .$$

By the definitions of these powers $10^3 = 1000$ and $10^{-2} = \frac{1}{100}$.

So that

$$10^3 \times 10^{-2} = 1000 \times \frac{1}{100} = 10 .$$

You see it checks. Try this one: $10^{-4} \times 10^{-5}$. By the law of exponents this is

$$10^{-4-5} = 10^{-9} = \frac{1}{1,000,000,000} .$$

By the definition,

$$10^{-4} = \frac{1}{10,000} ; \qquad 10^{-5} = \frac{1}{100,000}$$

and their product is indeed $\frac{1}{1,000,000,000}$. One more:

$$10^{-5} \times 10^5 = 10^{-5+5} = 10^0 = 1 ,$$

by the law of exponents and the meaning of the zeroth power. But also

$$10^{-5} = \frac{1}{100,000} , \qquad 10^5 = 100,000$$

and the product of the two is 1.

There is nothing special about 10. Suppose that a represents a number, positive or negative but not zero, and that n is another number. If we agree that

$$a^{-n} \text{ means } \frac{1}{a^n}$$

and

$$a^0 \text{ means } 1,$$

then we have introduced a system which guarantees that the law of exponents

$$a^m \times a^n = a^{m+n}$$

will be true no matter whether m and n are positive, negative, or zero. We can furthermore assert that

$$\frac{a^m}{a^n} = a^{m-n} .$$

The exponent notation with positive, negative, fractional and decimal exponents is hardly 300 years old. Although many men before had used the law of exponents, its explicit formulation is associated with the names of the English scientists Wallis and Sir Isaac Newton. Half the progress in the world comes from arranging facts in convenient bundles. Although this may only be a form of scientific "housekeeping," it sometimes takes the greatest minds to do it.

Problem Set 14

1. Multiply: 2.72×10^{-5} by 3.03×10^{8}.

2. Which is larger: 7^{-8} or 7^{-16}?

3. Determine the values of:

$$2^{-(2^3)}, \qquad 2^{(2^3)}, \qquad (-2)^{2^3}, \qquad (-2)^{-2^3}.$$

4. *Mighty Oaks From Little Acorns.* How can you show this: If a small quantity is added to itself a sufficiently large number of times the sum can be made to exceed any given large number. For instance if you add 10^{-10} to itself enough times the sum can be made greater than 10^{20}. This simple fact about numbers goes by the fancy name of *property of Archimedean order.* Mathematicians have been able to invent things which in many ways behave as ordinary numbers and yet which do not possess this property.

5. Establish: $\left(\dfrac{a}{b}\right)^{m} = \dfrac{a^m}{b^m}.$

6. In nuclear physics, one fermi $= 10^{-13}$ centimeters. One barn $= 10^{-24}$ square centimeters. How many square fermis in a barn?

15. The Large and the Small

There are small ants and there are large ants, but all are small compared to elephants. It is sometimes difficult to draw a dividing line between the large and the small, or the hot and the cold, or the right and the wrong. But it is frequently necessary to do so. As in Section 13, we shall say that a "small number" is one that is between 0 and 1 and a "large number" is one that is larger than one. The number one itself will be neither large nor small. Perhaps placing the dividing line at one seems peculiar. There are many numbers around 1, say $\frac{1}{2}$, $\frac{3}{4}$, $1\frac{1}{10}$, 2, etc., which seem neither large nor small. Perhaps it would be better to divide numbers into three categories: small, medium, and large. If this were done, then there would be difficulty in drawing the line between what is small and what is medium and between what is medium and what is large. Twice as much difficulty as before.

At any rate, let us accept the above definition of small and large and explore some of its consequences. Small and large stand in an inverse relationship to each other. The reciprocal of a large number (one divided by the number) is a small number, e.g., 88,922 is large, 1/88,922 is small. The reciprocal of a small number is a large number:

$$\frac{1}{\dfrac{1}{88,922}} = 88,922 \ .$$

As we know, when written in scientific notation, large numbers go with positive (or zero) powers of 10 and the small numbers go with negative powers of 10:

$$88,922 = 8.8922 \times 10^4 \ , \qquad \frac{1}{88,922} \approx 1.1246 \times 10^{-5} \ .$$

Small and large also have a special arithmetic of their own. It is easy to verify that

Large Number $\times$ Large Number = Large Number .

If a proof of this fact is wanted, one might argue as follows: Call the two large numbers M and N. By our definition, $N > 1$. (N is greater than 1.) Hence $M \times N > M \times 1$. But $M \times 1 = M$ and also $M > 1$. Putting these two facts together we conclude that $M \times N > 1$. This means the product $M \times N$ is also a large number.

We can also see (or prove) that:

Small Number $\times$ Small Number = Small Number
Large Number $\div$ Small Number = Large Number
Small Number $\div$ Large Number = Small Number

What about Small Number $\times$ Large Number? The answer here is not so simple. It depends upon the relative sizes of the numbers, e.g.,

Small Number		Large Number		
$\frac{1}{2}$	$\times$	$1\frac{1}{2}$	$= \frac{3}{4} =$	Small Number
$\frac{1}{2}$	$\times$	2	$= 1$	
$\frac{1}{2}$	$\times$	4	$= 2 =$	Large Number

The answer is indeterminate. It can be anything at all, small, one, or large. The same is true of Large ÷ Large and Small ÷ Small.

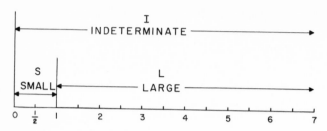

Figure 18. The large and the small

These facts can be summarized by a special kind of multiplication table. Let S designate the collection of all the numbers which are between 0 and 1. L will designate the collection of all numbers which are greater than 1. The letter I will designate the collection of all numbers greater than 0. We may think of S, L, and I, as representing "small," "large," and "indeterminate," but each of these symbols designates a certain set of numbers and not an individual number.

We are going to define a multiplication process for these sets of numbers. We will mean by $S \times L$ the collection of numbers that arises in this way: Take two numbers, one from S and one from L. Make this selection in all possible ways. The products which arise constitute a collection which we will designate by $S \times L$. What kind of products result? According to what we have said, any kind at all, small, one, or large. Therefore, we may write the equation

$$S \times L = I.$$

By $S \times I$ we shall designate the collection of all possible products which result from a multiplier in S and a multiplicand in I. It should be easy to see that

$$S \times I = I.$$

Here is the complete multiplication table for the symbols S, L, and I.

	S	L	I
S	S	I	I
L	I	L	I
I	I	I	I

Figure 19. A multiplication table for small, large, and indeterminate

The combinations that give rise to an *I* in this multiplication table are known as *indeterminate forms*, and far from being a curiosity are an important subject developed completely in the calculus.

We may also define division for the symbols *S*, *L*, and *I*. Following the pattern of multiplication, *S/L* will mean the set of all possible quotients which result from a dividend in *S* and a divisor in *L*. As we have mentioned

$$\frac{S}{L} = S .$$

Similar definitions are made for the other combinations of letters. Here is the complete division table.

		dividend		
		S	L	I
divisor	S	I	L	I
	L	S	I	I
	I	I	I	I

Figure 20. A division table for small, large, and indeterminate

This kind of multiplication and division is not like ordinary multiplication and division. Some strange things can happen. With ordinary numbers we can write, for instance,

$$\frac{6}{3} \times 3 = 6$$

and arrive at this answer by cancelling the 3's. Suppose we try this with S, L, and I. Is

$$\left(\frac{S}{L}\right) \times L = S ?$$

If we were to cancel the L's, we would certainly obtain S. But this is not correct. From the division table $S/L = S$, and from the multiplication table, $S \times L = I$. The correct answer is therefore I. Ordinary arithmetic is not always possible!

Problem Set 15

1. *Kipling's Problem.* "East is East and West is West and never the twain shall meet." What part of the surface of the earth is the eastern part and what part is the western part? Are there parts which are neither?

2. A town with 500 inhabitants is surely a small town. So is one with 501 inhabitants. Adding one more inhabitant to a small town won't make it a large town. Therefore, 501 inhabitants, 502 inhabitants, 503 inhabitants make a small town. Keep the argument up. We can obviously produce a large number of inhabitants and conclude that we still have a small town. What is wrong with this argument?

3. There is an observation station exactly at the South Pole. What time zone should it be in?

4. *A Principle of Relativity.* Consider two objects which are of different sizes. Show that by choosing a unit of measurement properly, the numbers which represent the sizes of the two objects may (a) be both large, (b) be both small, or (c) one will be large and the other small.

5. Evaluate $\left(\frac{L}{L}\right) \times L$.

6. Show that $\left(\frac{L}{S}\right) \times S = L \times \left(\frac{S}{S}\right)$.

7. Give meaning to S^2, L^2, I^2. Show that $S^2 = S$, $L^2 = L$, $I^2 = I$.

8. Do the same for S^n, L^n, I^n where n is a positive integer.

9. Prove that the first law of exponents $a^m \times a^n = a^{m+n}$ is true where m and n are positive integers and where a designates any of the symbols S, L, or I.

10. What about the second law of exponents?

11. Give meaning to $\sqrt{S}$, $\sqrt{L}$, $\sqrt{I}$. Evaluate these expressions.

12. If a and b designate any of the symbols S, L, or I, is it true that

$$\sqrt{a \times b} = \sqrt{a} \times \sqrt{b}, \quad \text{and} \quad \sqrt{\frac{a}{b}} = \frac{\sqrt{a}}{\sqrt{b}} ?$$

16. Division by Zero: The Road to Paradox

The larger a number, the smaller its reciprocal. The smaller a number, the larger its reciprocal. We can produce larger and larger quantities by dividing 1 by a smaller and smaller quantity:

$$\frac{1}{1} = 1$$

$$\frac{1}{.1} = 10$$

$$\frac{1}{.01} = 100$$

$$\frac{1}{.001} = 1000 .$$

Why not go the whole way and divide 1 by 0?

$$\frac{1}{0} = ?$$

This ought to produce something interesting! The largest number in the world, perhaps. Or who knows what? Unfortunately, this good idea can cause trouble. Division by zero cannot be defined in a meaningful and consistent way in mathematics. Suppose we have performed a division, $\frac{369}{9} = 41$, and want to check the answer. One way is to multiply back: $9 \times 41 = 369$. Suppose now that someone has written $\frac{1}{0}$ and gives us the job of finding a meaning for this. It cannot be a number, for if

$$\frac{1}{0} = n$$

where n is some number, and we attempt to check this equation by multiplying back, we find $1 = 0 \times n = 0$. In other words, $1 = 0$, and this is false. The equation does not check. The same thing will happen if any other number different from zero is divided by zero.

The division of zero by zero is exceptional. Suppose we write

$$\frac{0}{0} = 6$$

and check by multiplying back. $0 = 6 \times 0 = 0$. Check. 6 must be the answer. But what is so wonderful about 6? Why not 184?

$$\frac{0}{0} = 184 .$$

Multiplying back, $0 = 0 \times 184 = 0$. Check. This work seems to imply that $\frac{0}{0}$ can be anything at all. Such a result could hardly be useful. For these reasons, division by zero is abandoned in mathematics.

The cardinal sin of mathematics is the derivation of a contradiction, that is, the proof of a statement which is palpably false. It is one of the principles of logic that granted one contradiction, any statement at all can be proved. One rotten apple spoils the barrel!

As we have seen, division by zero can result in a contradiction. When it is blatant and stares one in the eye, it can be avoided. Since

$$6 \times 0 = 4 \times 0 ,$$

we obtain, by dividing both sides of the equation by zero,

$$6 = 4 .$$

Sometimes the division by zero is camouflaged. Let

$$x = 1;$$

then

$$x^2 - x = x^2 - 1.$$

Therefore

$$x(x - 1) = (x - 1)(x + 1) .$$

Divide by the factor $(x - 1)$:

$$x = x + 1 .$$

But

$$x = 1$$

and hence

$$1 = 2 .$$

In higher mathematics, this error can turn up in quite subtle ways, and it may be comforting to know that some famous scientists, including Einstein, have fallen into its trap.

Though division by zero is ruled out, it is amusing to play with symbols especially when they are vague and their meaning not well understood. This can be a dangerous business. But it can also be the source of exciting discovery, and important results in mathematics have come about in this way.

We divided 1 by 0 in a futile hunt for the largest number. What we obtained could not be a number at all. But is it large, even if it is not a number? Admittedly, this question sounds like nonsense and may be nonsense, but let us look into it anyway. Is $6 < \frac{1}{0}$? Is

$10^{100,000} < \frac{1}{0}$? How can we possibly decide? If we were dealing with ordinary numbers it would be easy. An inequality such as $6 < \frac{27}{4}$ can be checked by multiplying both members of the inequality by 4 and checking the resulting simple inequality $6 \times 4 < 27$. Check. Now start with $6 < \frac{1}{0}$. Multiplying by 0 yields $6 \times 0 < 1$ or $0 < 1$. This is true. Since (any number) $\times 0 < 1$, it "follows" that any number $< \frac{1}{0}$. Whatever kind of thing $\frac{1}{0}$ is must be large, for it seems to be greater than any number whatever.

Let us try to "increase" $\frac{1}{0}$ by adding 1 to it.

$$\frac{1}{0} + 1 = ?$$

How shall we add? If we were dealing with ordinary fractions, we would put them over a common denominator

$$\frac{2}{3} + 1 = \frac{2 + (3 \times 1)}{3} = \frac{5}{3}.$$

If we do this, we find

$$\frac{1}{0} + 1 = \frac{1 + (0 \times 1)}{0} = \frac{1}{0}.$$

In other words, whatever $\frac{1}{0}$ is, if you add 1 to it, it is unchanged. How natural! $\frac{1}{0}$ is so "large" that adding 1 does not affect it one bit. It is like adding a drop to the ocean, only more so. If we form $\frac{1}{0} + 10^{10}$, the same reasoning leads to the equation $\frac{1}{0} + 10^{10} = \frac{1}{0}$. 10^{10} is also a mere drop compared with $\frac{1}{0}$.

Is $\frac{2}{0}$ greater than $\frac{1}{0}$? Is it twice as large? Take the inequality $\frac{2}{0} > \frac{1}{0}$ and multiply up by the denominators to check. We get a surprise: $2 \times 0 > 1 \times 0$. This is $0 > 0$ and so it does not check. Is, perhaps $\frac{2}{0} < \frac{1}{0}$? Multiplying up yields $0 < 0$. Again, it does not check. Perhaps $\frac{2}{0} = \frac{1}{0}$. Multiply up. $2 \times 0 = 1 \times 0$ or $0 = 0$. Check. In the same way, we could "conclude" that $10^{10}/0 = 1/0$. $\frac{1}{0}$ is so large that multiplying it by positive numbers has no effect whatever.

At this point, readers who have looked ahead in mathematics may say, "But what about infinity? Is not $\frac{1}{0} = $ infinity?" There are a number of different ways in which the notion of infinity has been introduced into mathematics meaningfully and usefully. In no case does infinity play the role of the largest integer. These theories lie beyond elementary arithmetic though they are not particularly difficult. We must refer the interested readers to other books. There they will find proper formulations of the facts of the last several paragraphs which seem at once to be so fascinating and so fraudulent.

Problem Set 16

1. Using division by zero "prove" that: $63702 = 929,753\frac{1}{2}$.

2. Assuming that the Fourth of July is in February, set up a chain of logical reasoning to conclude that a zebra is a bird.

3. "Prove," by using the law of exponents and division by zero, that 0^0 can be any number at all.

4. *Desk Infinities.* A certain desk calculator can divide one ten digit number by another. It does this essentially by subtracting the divisor from the dividend over and over again and observing how many subtractions were required to reduce the dividend to zero. For instance, in $27 \div 3$ it forms 24, 21, 18, 15, 12, 9, 6, 3, 0 and then stops, counting 9 subtractions in all. It is possible to divide 9,999,999,999 by 1 on the machine. If the machine can make 1300 subtractions per minute, estimate how long it would take to perform this division.

5. It is possible to go through the motions of dividing 1 by 0 on a desk calculator. What do you suppose happens?

PART II

Large Numbers at Work

17. The Long Long Trail of π

What is the longest number that has ever been computed? As of early 1960, it is very probably the sum of the infinite series of fractions

$$1 + \frac{1}{1} + \frac{1}{1 \times 2} + \frac{1}{1 \times 2 \times 3} + \frac{1}{1 \times 2 \times 3 \times 4} + \cdots$$

This is a number which is designated in mathematics by the letter e. Its value to 12 decimals is 2.718281828459.

In December 1952, Professor D. J. Wheeler computed the value of e to 60,000 decimals on the ILLIAC, an electronic computing machine located at the University of Illinois in Urbana, Illinois. It took the machine 40 hours to complete the job. What is behind such lengthy computations? Why are they done? Of what use are they? To arrive at an answer we must plunge deeply into the history of mathematics.

The number e now holds the record for long computations, but we are going to tell our story and formulate our answer for another famous number for which tremendously long computations have been made: the number π. The number π is older by several thousand years and it is more familiar. Its tale is one of the most fascinating in the whole of mathematics. For these reasons, it will serve our purpose better.

There are certain ideas which run like scarlet threads through the fabric of mathematics. Each age finds its own particular interest in them and treats them in its own way. One of these is the number 3.1415926535 . . . which has come to be designated by the Greek letter π (pronounced pie). Perhaps it is more readily recognized in the rougher, but simpler approximation $3\frac{1}{7}$. π is the circle number. Whenever there are circles to be measured or figures that have circles in them, such as spheres, cylinders, cones, π is sure to be of importance. It was recognized at an early period in history that the ratio of the circumference of a circle to its diameter is the same, regardless of the size of the circle. This ratio is π:

$$\pi = \frac{\text{circumference of circle}}{\text{diameter of circle}}$$

(see Figure 3).

The Greek mathematicians two thousand and more years ago concerned themselves with several problems relating to π: (1) What is its exact value? (2) Is it possible to construct, using a ruler and a compass and subject to conditions whose precise formulation will be omitted, a square whose area is that of a given circle? This is the problem of squaring the circle. Along with the trisection of the angle and the duplication of the cube, it is one of the three famous mathematical problems of antiquity. The problems (1) and (2) are related to each other.

The ancients used a variety of values for the number π; some good, some bad. A result which has a modern flavor is one given by Archimedes. He was able to prove that

$$3\frac{10}{71} < \pi < 3\frac{1}{7}.$$

The method he employed was a good one, that of approximating the contour of the circle by polygons. Since Archimedes knew how to compute the lengths of the sides of regular polygons with great accuracy, he was able to obtain information about circles. He used polygons with 96 sides. Archimedes' result stated above is modern in outlook, precisely because it is phrased as an *inequality*. When mathematicians are faced with quantities which are hard to estimate or compute, they try, at least, to pin them in between two other quantities which they can compute. The Greeks were not able to obtain an exact rational value for π. The reason is simply this; π is not a rational fraction. It is a more complicated number. Though some Greek mathematicians might have suspected this, none proved it.

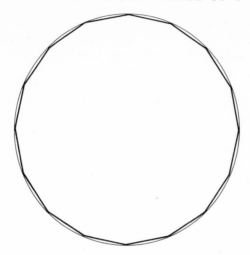

Figure 21. A circle approximated by a regular polygon of 16 sides

They had no luck with squaring the circle. There were many who tried. Perhaps they were lured on by a beautiful but misleading discovery of Hippocrates (430 B.C.) who found that the area of certain crescent shaped figures was equal to that of a certain square. (See Fig. 33.)

Now if a crescent can be squared, why not a circle? After all, a circle is a far smoother, far simpler figure than a crescent. But though men sought continually for a construction which would square the circle, it could not be found. Repeated failures produced the word "circle-squarer" and this meant to the Greeks as it does to us a person who tries to accomplish the impossible. It took an additional two thousand years to prove that squaring the circle was impossible. Indeed, this proof was not achieved until 1882. The fact that the problem was not solved for such a long time shows how deep it lay and how easy it is to raise mathematical questions that are extremely difficult to answer.

The ancients do not appear to have been successful or interested in computing π very accurately. Perhaps their method, somewhat cumbersome though theoretically perfect, prevented it. Perhaps they were hampered by their system of numbers which was even more cumbersome. Perhaps they were too practical minded and could find no situation which demanded such precise knowledge. The most precise value computed was 3.1416. This was worked out by the mathematician and astronomer Ptolemy about 150 A.D.

Figure 22. π in the days of classic splendor (200 B.C.)

Several hundred years later the great Roman civilization came to an end. The world was dominated by less civilized peoples and new concerns. The computation of π and the speculation as to its character lay dormant for about 1400 years and then were awakened to full vigor by the fresh currents of Renaissance thought and by the scientific revolution which followed soon after.

One of the accomplishments of the intervening centuries was the perfection of the art of computing by the introduction of the decimal notation for integers and fractional quantities. The resulting ease in computing was soon reflected in improvements in the approximation of π. The ancient method of approximating the circle by polygons was employed and by 1579 Viete had computed the value of π to 10 figures. In 1593 Romanus gave its value to 16 figures. In 1610

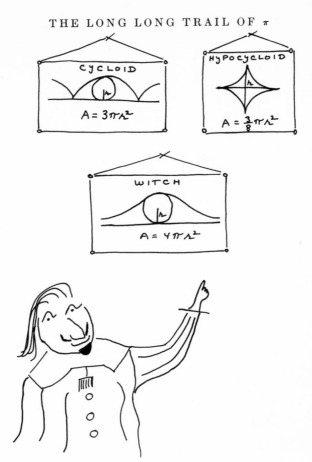

Figure 23. π in the early days of the calculus (1600's)

van Ceulen gave it to 33 figures. In 1621 Snell computed it to 35 figures. In order to obtain this accuracy, Snell had to employ regular polygons possessing 2^{30} sides. Of course, it was not necessary for him to draw such a figure, but his computations refer to such a polygon. These long computations were made partly out of sheer exuberance at being able to carry them out and partly in the hope that π might turn out to be a fraction, though a complicated one, which could be discovered in this way.

The relation between numbers that are fractions and their decimal equivalent is this. Every fraction, when expressed as a decimal, either "comes out even" as

$$\frac{1}{8} = .125$$

or becomes cyclic; that is, its digits recur over and over again in a fixed cycle. This is the case with

$$\frac{1}{3} = .3333\ldots$$

where 3 is repeated indefinitely, or with

$$\frac{1}{7} = .142857\ 142857\ 142857\ldots$$

where a whole group of 6 digits is repeated.

The reverse statement is also true. A decimal whose digits recur cyclically must be a fraction. If π were computed to many many places, and the digits began to recur, then this would suggest strongly that it is a fraction. It would not be a conclusive proof, but once the right answer were known, it might spur the hunt for a proper argument. This did not happen. No matter how far the computations were pushed the digits did not recur cyclically.

Two great mathematical subjects were developed during the seventeenth century, analytic geometry and the calculus. They had an immediate effect on π. π was freed from the circle. Many curves were invented and studied, and it was found that their areas could be expressed in terms of π. An ellipse has a formula for its area which involves π (a fact known to the Greeks) but this is also true of the cycloidal arch, the hypocycloid, the witch, and many many other curves.

It appears that π is not the exclusive property of circles. Indeed, by the end of the 18th century it was known that every closed contour, smooth or with corners, can be related to π. This can be accomplished by means of the formula

$$\frac{1}{2} \int_C \frac{x\,dy - y\,dx}{x^2 + y^2} = \pi\ .$$

The letter C designates any curve which winds around a reference point $(x = 0,\ y = 0)$ once. The symbol $\int_C$ is a *line integral* and represents a kind of infinite process of addition which takes place on the curve. The circle number became an area number, and then it became a "rotation" number, for the formula above can be interpreted as stating that as a point P traverses completely a simple closed curve, the line OP joining it with an interior point O rotates through 360°.

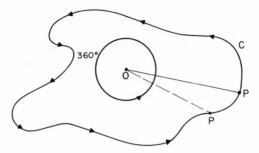

Figure 24. The rotation number

Finally, π broke through the confines of geometry altogether. It would scarcely be possible to list all the places in mathematics where it is of importance today.

One of the major chapters of calculus deals with *infinite series*. Every one who has dealt with decimals knows about such things. When $\frac{1}{3}$ is expressed as an unending decimal

$$\frac{1}{3} = .33333 \ldots$$

this means that

$$\frac{1}{3} = \frac{3}{10} + \frac{3}{100} + \frac{3}{1000} + \frac{3}{10,000} + \cdots$$

and is an example of an infinite series, or an unending addition process. Many infinite series relating to π were discovered beginning in the late 1600's. Here are a few which date from this era of mathematics:

$$\frac{\pi}{4} = 1 - \frac{1}{3} + \frac{1}{5} - \frac{1}{7} + \frac{1}{9} - \frac{1}{11} + \frac{1}{13} - \cdots \qquad \text{(Gregory, 1671)}$$

$$\frac{\pi^2}{6} = 1 + \frac{1}{1^2} + \frac{1}{2^2} + \frac{1}{3^2} + \frac{1}{4^2} + \cdots \qquad \text{(Euler, 1736)}$$

$$\pi = 16 \left(\frac{1}{5} - \frac{1}{3 \times 5^3} + \frac{1}{5 \times 5^5} - \frac{1}{7 \times 5^7} + \frac{1}{9 \times 5^9} - \cdots \right)$$

$$-4 \left(\frac{1}{239} - \frac{1}{3 \times 239^3} + \frac{1}{5 \times 239^5} - \cdots \right) \qquad \text{(Machin, 1706)}$$

$$\pi = 2\sqrt{3} \left(1 - \frac{1}{3 \times 3} + \frac{1}{5 \times 3^2} - \frac{1}{7 \times 3^5} \cdots \right) \qquad \text{(Sharp, 1717)}$$

Figure 25. Some infinite series for π

The relation between π and these series of simple fractions is a constant source of wonder. With the discovery of such formulas, which are as remote from geometry as anything one can imagine, π became the property of all mathematics and has remained so till this day.

Some of the series listed here are remarkably well adapted for computation and through them, π was obtained to a great many figures. In 1699 Sharp computed its value to 72 figures. In 1706 Machin computed its value to 101 figures. The search for the fraction to represent π exactly went on. In 1761 it came to an end. The German mathematician Lambert proved that π is an irrational number. It is not a fraction; its decimal digits are not cyclic. Until recently no simple proof of Lambert's theorem was known, but in 1947 Professor I. Niven of the University of Oregon found a proof which is within the grasp of anyone who has studied integral calculus. In a certain sense, what is surprising is not that it took from the Greeks to Lambert to prove that π is not a fraction, but that it didn't take longer. This sort of mathematical problem has turned out to be remarkably difficult. There are no general rules of procedure. And there are numerous problems of a similar type which have thus far defied solution.

There is the problem of the number called *Euler's constant*. This number is generally designated by the Greek letter γ (gamma) and can be defined in the following way:

$$\gamma = \lim_{n \to \infty} \left(1 + \frac{1}{2} + \frac{1}{3} + \frac{1}{4} + \ldots + \frac{1}{n} \right) - \log n \ .$$

The first few decimals of this number are

$$\gamma = .577215664 \ldots .$$

It has been computed to more than 350 figures. Its decimal expression shows no sign of cyclic behavior and the same question can be raised: *is γ a fraction?* Mathematicians think it is not. But at the present time (1960) the problem is unsolved. Its position is the same as the position of π before Lambert. Since γ is considerably less important than π, correspondingly less effort has been spent in trying to solve the problem.

Let us return to π. Lambert proved that it could not be a simple fraction. This answered the first of the questions raised by the

Greeks. But the second question, whether or not the circle could be squared using ruler and compass alone was still an unanswered one. One could construct a length or area that, although not expressible as a fraction, could be expressed in terms of fractions and square roots. The problem here was to show that π cannot be expressed with fractions and square roots.

A stronger conjecture was put forth: π *is a transcendental number.* That is to say, π could not satisfy exactly equations of the type

$$\pi^2 = 10$$
$$22\pi^4 = 2143$$
$$9\pi^4 - 240\pi^2 + 1492 = 0 .$$

These are equations involving simple integers with powers of π. It was easy to show that if a quantity were constructible with ruler and compass, then it must satisfy such an equation.

At the beginning of the 19th century the notion of a transcendental number was new. In fact, mathematicians of the day could not point to a single number and say, "We have proved that this number is transcendental." The subject had not yet been enriched by the ideas of George Cantor in Germany who in the 1880's showed by a brilliant but ridiculously simple argument that practically every real number is transcendental! The first transcendental number was found by the French mathematician, J. Liouville, in 1851. It is the number given by the infinite series:

$$\frac{1}{10} + \frac{1}{10^{1\times2}} + \frac{1}{10^{1\times2\times3}} + \frac{1}{10^{1\times2\times3\times4}} + \cdots$$

The decimal form of Liouville's number is easily written down. It is:

$$.110001000000000000000000100 \ldots$$

and has a one in the 1st, 2nd, 6th, 24th, 120th, etc. places and zeros elsewhere. Liouville succeeded in finding a whole class of numbers that were all transcendental, but unfortunately π was not one of them. In the 1850's the status of the conjecture about π was shaky. There was every reason to think that π was transcendental. But the proof was still lacking. It required another thirty years. In 1882, a proof was finally obtained by the German mathematician F. Lindemann. π is transcendental. The problem of squaring the circle was conclusively shown to be impossible.

Ueber die Zahl π.*)

Von

F. Lindemann in Freiburg i. Br.

Bei der Vergeblichkeit der so ausserordentlich zahlreichen Versuche**), die Quadratur des Kreises mit Cirkel und Lineal auszuführen, hält man allgemein die Lösung der bezeichneten Aufgabe für unmöglich; es fehlte aber bisher ein Beweis dieser Unmöglichkeit; nur die Irrationalität von π und von π^2 ist festgestellt. Jede mit Cirkel und Lineal ausführbare Construction lässt sich mittelst algebraischer Einkleidung zurückführen auf die Lösung von linearen und quadratischen Gleichungen, also auch auf die Lösung einer Reihe von quadratischen Gleichungen, deren erste rationale Zahlen zu Coefficienten hat, während die Coefficienten jeder folgenden nur solche irrationale Zahlen enthalten, die durch Auflösung der vorhergehenden Gleichungen eingeführt sind. Die Schlussgleichung wird also durch wiederholtes Quadriren übergeführt werden können in eine Gleichung geraden Grades, deren Coefficienten rationale Zahlen sind. Man wird sonach die Unmöglichkeit der Quadratur des Kreises darthun, wenn man nachweist, dass *die Zahl π überhaupt nicht Wurzel einer algebraischen Gleichung irgend welchen Grades mit rationalen Coefficienten sein kann*. Den dafür nöthigen Beweis zu erbringen, ist im Folgenden versucht worden.

Figure 26. From the first page of a mathematical classic.
F. Lindemann's article of 1882 put an end to 2500 years of speculation.

While all this theoretical work was being carried out, the computation of the decimal value of π was also pushed forward. In 1794, Vega, a man who had computed a famous table of logarithms, calculated the value of π to 137 figures. In 1844, the lightning computer Dase, who worked under the supervision of the great German mathematician, Gauss, came out with 201 figures. In 1853, Rutherford, an Englishman, produced 441 figures, and in 1873, Shanks, another Englishman, produced 707 (527 correct). After Lindemann's proof of 1882, this activity ceased. The computation of π went to sleep once again.

It really seemed as if the computation of π had come to the end of the trail. It had been pushed to limits which made further work intolerably difficult and tedious, and the last vestige of a reason for additional computation had long disappeared. To go further one would need improved means for computing and a significant reason for doing so.

Mathematics has curious powers of regeneration. In the late 1940's two new mathematical streams met and led to renewed computation of π. The development of high speed electronic computing equipment gave the means for computation; inquiries as to the digits of π, not what they are individually, but how they behave statistically, provided the motive.

Problem Set 17

1. Verify that

$$3\frac{10}{71} < \pi < 3\frac{1}{7}$$

specifies π correctly to 2 figures.

2. Verify that $\frac{355}{113}$ specifies π correctly to 6 figures.

3. Is π closest to $3\frac{1}{7}$, $3\frac{10}{71}$, or to the average of these two numbers?

4. If Snell's regular polygon of 2^{30} sides were inscribed in the equator of the earth show (by dividing the circumference into this many parts) that each side would be about $1\frac{1}{2}$ inches long.

5. The equations $\pi^2 = 10$, $22\pi^4 = 2143$, $9\pi^4 - 240\pi^2 + 1492 = 0$ that were used to illustrate the meaning of transcendental numbers were not pulled out of a hat. They are famous in the history of π. While they are not exact statements of equality, they are approximately correct. The first is the least exact, the third is better, and the second is the best of all. By using a very good approximation of π in the left-hand side, determine how nearly correct these equations are. The first equation was known to the ancients. The second was discovered in 1914 by the famous Indian mathematician, Srinivasa Ramanujan (1887–1920). The third comes from a geometric construction which squares the circle approximately and which was discovered in 1685 by Adam Kochansky, a Jesuit employed as librarian to King John of Poland.

6. *The White House Ellipse.* A U.S. Geological Survey map of Washington, D.C. shows that there is an elliptical park in front of the White House. The map is drawn to the scale 1: 31,680. The semi-major axis, a, of the ellipse measures $\frac{13}{64}$ in. The semi-minor axis, b, measures $\frac{11}{64}$ in. Use the formula for the area A of an ellipse given in Figure 22 (page 58) and compute approximately the number of acres in the park.

18. The Long Trail Continued: Computing Machines Meet Normal Numbers.

(a) *Computing machines.* Computing, as we know, is the art of manipulating numbers. Arithmetic learned in elementary school deals partly with the techniques of computing and partly with the application of these techniques to various problems. Addition, subtraction, multiplication, division and square roots are the processes learned in the grades. Modern technology and science pose problems which require elaborate combinations of these basic operations. Make no mistake about it; computing is not an easy task. It is long and it is tedious; and, what is more, people are prone to make mistakes carrying it out. There are very few short cuts that amount to anything. Some gifted people possess an uncanny ability of "lightning" calculation. By some inner process, largely unexplained, they are able to arrive at the answers to difficult arithmetic problems with great speed and accuracy. Unfortunately, ordinary mortals—and this includes most men who are professional mathematicians—have not been able to acquire this lightning ability.

It is no wonder that most people avoid computing like the plague, and it is no wonder that mechanical devices have been developed to make computing fast and easy. Small computing machines are now omnipresent. When I was a boy and bought a bag of groceries, the clerk invariably wrote the prices of the items down on the bag and added them up. Today, the adding machine is built into the cash register and it spits out a sum which neither the shopper nor the clerk bother to check. Just as today is an age of incessant travel and one's legs are apt to atrophy from want of walking, so also today is an age of calculation in which one's arithmetic abilities are hardly ever exercised.

Figure 27. The first digital computer

The list of computing devices that have been employed over the centuries is a long one. Abacuses and counting boards of all sorts, sticks, rods, computing pieces have all been and still are employed. Tables of addition and multiplication, of quarter squares, of logarithms have had their place on computers' desks. The slide rule and the nomogram have their areas of utility. The small electric computing machine is much employed today. One popular model is capable of addition, subtraction, multiplication, division, square root extraction and operates with 10 digit numbers. A generation ago, these instruments could be found only in a few laboratories; today's model has penetrated to lumber yards and drafting offices.

But the wonder of the age and the weathercock of the future is the high speed electronic computing machine, a child of the tube and the transistor, incredibly fast, accurate, and versatile. These machines have opened a new chapter in the long history of computing, and very likely, a new chapter in the history of the scientific revolution.

A mechanical computer has gears that are driven by an electric motor. How does it work—not internally—but from the point of view of the user? If you want to add numbers, you punch the first number in on the keyboard, and then depress a + button. This enters the first number on a blank of numbers at the top of the machine. You then punch the second number on the keyboard, depress the + button, and now the sum of the two numbers appears at the top. Subtraction is similar. To multiply, you enter the multiplicand on the keyboard and then punch special keys for the multiplier. The product appears now at the top. Division is about the same. If you must do a long computation such as

$$21.6 + \frac{48 \times 6193 \times (.00278)^2}{(2.0492)^2 + (3.0708)^2}$$

then you must enter and reenter the machine, and mark down a sequence of partial answers as you go along. Mechanical computers carry out one shot computations. Two ten digit numbers can be added in about 15 seconds and can be multiplied in about 20 seconds.

An electronic computer has powers that exceed enormously those of its mechanical cousin. In the first place, it can do more than arithmetic operations. It can treat numbers as cardinals, as ordinals, and as tags; it can also do "logical" operations such as checking, and combining tags. It has a large memory unit in which it stores instructions on what to do, numbers on which to operate, and various partial, interim answers which may be needed. It does not operate on a one shot principle. It operates sequentially, one computation after another, according to the instructions which have been prepared for it. In the course of the program of computation it can make decisions as to what to do next; in many problems, what to do next may very well depend on what information has been obtained up to that time. It can change its own procedural instructions should the need arise. Sequences of thousands or millions of computations can be done with one push of the button. Finally, it operates with lightning speed; two numbers may be added on the IBM 704 in 10^{-5} seconds and may be multiplied in 4×10^{-5} seconds. Logical operations are even faster.

Electronic machines not only do computation for scientific purposes, but do many useful things. They can keep track of the contents of a warehouse or the passenger reservations on an airline. They are good at looking up information that has been stored away. They have been made to translate one language into another—not very well at the moment, but there is every reason to believe that they will be able to do this with increasing competence. Computers can track satellites, simulate the motion of an airplane for training pilots, and direct assembly lines. They can even compose string quartets and play chess.

Figure 28. An electronic digital computing machine. The IBM 7090 Data Processing System. In one second, this machine can perform any of the following: 229,000 additions or subtractions, 39,500 multiplications, or 32,700 divisions.
Courtesy of the IBM Corporation.

To do these things, a computing machine must be instructed properly. To compose a list of instructions may be a long and painstaking process requiring months and even years of labor on the part of computer mathematicians. When properly instructed, the computing machine can do many things which rival or even exceed the abilities of the human brain. It has set philosophers wondering as to just what the proper activity of human beings is.

(b) *Normal numbers.* When we take a look at a great many figures of the decimal expression for π there is one thing that surely strikes us immediately. The digits seem to follow one another in a completely mixed up and unfathomable way. There is no simple way of predicting in advance what a given digit of π will be. For instance, there is no way of telling in advance what the millionth digit of π is, short of performing a complete computation in which all the digits up to the 1,000,000th have also been calculated. In the early part of this century the Dutch mathematician L. E. J. Brouwer was pondering over the logic and the philosophy of mathematics. To illustrate a point he was making, he wanted an example of a mathematical problem so difficult that its solution in the next ten or twenty years seemed unlikely. Here is the problem that Brouwer thought up: In the decimal expression for π, do we ever come to a place where a thousand consecutive digits are all zero? The answer was and still is unknown. Since π had had such a long record as a source of hard problems, it was no accident that Brouwer turned to it for his problem.

About the same time, Émile Borel, a French mathematician, was making important discoveries about the real number system (that is, the recurrent and non-recurrent decimals). At one point in his work, he must have been led to thoughts such as these: there are numbers which are fractions (rational numbers) and numbers which are not fractions (irrational numbers). When expressed as decimals, the fractions give rise to a simple recurrent pattern. The irrational numbers do not; they are frequently, though not always, a mere jumble of digits. This seems to be the case with π, but also with many other irrational numbers such as $\sqrt{2}$, $\sqrt{3}$, etc. In π, if one looks for a single digit, say the digit 1, it appears in the 1st place after the point, in the 3rd place after the point, in the 37th place, the 40th place, 49th place, 68th place, 94th place, 95th place, and so forth. No apparent order. But is it possible that the digit 1 appears a fixed fraction of the time on the average? What fraction? Why, $\frac{1}{10}$ of course. This would mean that if we took 100 places of π.

1 would appear about 10 times. If we took 1,000 places of π, 1 would appear very nearly 100 times. If we took 10,000 places of π, 1 would appear very very nearly 1,000 times, and so on. Such statistical regularity might very well be possible.

By considerations such as these, Borel was led to define a *normal* number. A normal number is one in which each digit appears on the average $\frac{1}{10}$ of the time. But more than this, each pair of digits (such as 27 or 00) appears $\frac{1}{100}$ of the time on the average. Each triple of digits, such as 116, 299, or 000, appears $\frac{1}{1,000}$ of the time. And so on for each group of 4, 5, . . . digits.

With this interesting definition as a guide, Borel divided all numbers into two types, those that are normal and those that are not normal. He was able to prove that almost all numbers are normal. This is as it should be, of course, since normal characteristics of any sort ought to be in the majority. The curious thing is that no fraction is normal! How can it be, when it is a repeating decimal? For instance, in the decimal expression for

$$\frac{4}{11} = .3636363636 \ldots ,$$

half of the digits are 3's and half are 6's. The digits 0, 1, 2, 4, 5, 7, 8, 9 do not get their proper share. Even if all the digits were to get their proper share as would be the case with the fraction

$$\frac{137174210}{1111111111} = .1234567890123456789012345567890 \ldots ,$$

then combinations of digits such as 00 or 11 which never appear would not receive theirs.

An example of a normal number is the number obtained when the integers are written down in their natural order behind a decimal point:

.123456789101112131415161718192021 . . . .

This number has all digits in their proper proportions and all blocks of digits in their proper proportions.

To work backwards from familiar irrational numbers and to prove that they are normal is a much harder task. It is not known whether such numbers as $\sqrt{2}$, $\sqrt{3}$, e or π are normal. If, for instance, π were normal, we could conclude from this fact that a block of 1000 zeros occurs in its decimal representation not only once, but infinitely often and with an average frequency of 1 in 10^{1000}. You can now see that to prove that π is a normal number much more is required than to answer the question that Brouwer raised. And this alone has been considered a task of the first magnitude.

With these questions of normality at the back of many mathematicians' minds, it was natural enough for high speed computing machines to meet up with π. And meet up they did. The year was 1949. The place was the Army's Aberdeen Proving Ground at Aberdeen, Maryland. The computing machine was called the ENIAC. The ENIAC was first programmed to compute e, for its series is less complicated. Over the Fourth of July weekend, e was computed to 2000 places. By the time Labor Day had rolled around, the program for π was ready. With only 70 hours of machine time, 2036 figures were produced! Compare this with the old days in which a van Ceulen might work a lifetime to come up with 33 figures.

In 1954, at the Watson Scientific Laboratory in New York City, π was computed on the NORC computer to 3093 decimals. The speeds of computing machines had increased so much in the intervening five years that this computation required only 13 minutes of machine time.

In 1959, in Paris, France, π was computed to 10,000 decimals on an IBM 704 computer. The machine instructions were prepared by Mr. F. Genuys who did it as a training problem. The computing time required: 1 hour, 40 minutes. In England in the same year, Mr. Felton, using a Ferranti PEGASUS, computed π to 10,007 decimals. Genuys' machine instructions allow it to be computed to 20,000 decimals and he has estimated that it would require 6 machine hours to carry out the calculation. There are so many computers in so many different lands today, it is hard to know about all the activity in this direction. We may yet see π to 100,000 or even to 1,000,000 places within the next five years.

What about the distribution of the digits of π? These long computations indicate strongly what mathematicians feel must be the case, that π is a normal number and exhibits no preference for any digit or combination of digits. For instance, in the first 2000 digits to the right of the decimal point there are

182	0's	205 ·	5's
212	1's	200	6's
207	2's	197	7's
189	3's	202	8's
195	4's	211	9's.

THE LORE OF LARGE NUMBERS

Four thousand decimals of π

CALCUL DE PI SUR ORDINATEUR IBM 704

```
3,14159 26535 89793 23846 26433 83279 50288 41971 69399 37510
58209 74944 59230 78164 06286 20899 86280 34825 34211 70679
82148 08651 32823 06647 09384 46095 50582 23172 53594 08128
48111 74502 84102 70193 85211 05559 64462 29489 54930 38196
44288 10975 66593 34461 28475 64823 37867 83165 27120 19091

45648 56692 34603 48610 45432 66482 13393 60726 02491 41273
72458 70066 06315 58817 48815 20920 96282 92540 91715 36436
78925 90360 01133 05305 48820 46652 13841 46951 94151 16094
33057 27036 57595 91953 09218 61173 81932 61179 31051 18548
07446 23799 62749 56735 18857 52724 89122 79381 83011 94912

98336 73362 44065 66430 86021 39494 63952 24737 19070 21798
60943 70277 05392 17176 29317 67523 84674 81846 76694 05132
00056 81271 45263 56082 77857 71342 75778 96091 73637 17872
14684 40901 22495 34301 46549 58537 10507 92279 68925 89235
42019 95611 21290 21960 86403 44181 59813 62977 47713 09960

51870 72113 49999 99837 29780 49951 05973 17328 16096 31859
50244 59455 34690 83026 42522 30825 33446 85035 26193 11881
71010 00313 78387 52886 58753 32083 81420 61717 76691 47303
59825 34904 28755 46873 11595 62863 88235 37875 93751 95778
18577 80532 17122 68066 13001 92787 66111 95909 21642 01989

38095 25720 10654 85863 27886 59361 53381 82796 82303 01952
03530 18529 68995 77362 25994 13891 24972 17752 83479 13151
55748 57242 45415 06959 50829 53311 68617 27855 88907 50983
81754 63746 49393 19255 06040 09277 01671 13900 98488 24012
85836 16035 63707 66010 47101 81942 95559 61989 46767 83744

94482 55379 77472 68471 04047 53464 62080 46684 25906 94912
93313 67702 89891 52104 75216 20569 66024 05803 81501 93511
25338 24300 35587 64024 74964 73263 91419 92726 04269 92279
67823 54781 63600 93417 21641 21992 45863 15030 28618 29745
55706 74983 85054 94588 58692 69956 90927 21079 75093 02955

32116 53449 87202 75596 02364 80665 49911 98818 34797 75356
63698 07426 54252 78625 51818 41757 46728 90977 77279 38000
81647 06001 61452 49192 17321 72147 72350 14144 19735 68548
16136 11573 52552 13347 57418 49468 43852 33239 07394 14333
45477 62416 86251 89835 69485 56209 92192 22184 27255 02542

56887 67179 04946 01653 46680 49886 27232 79178 60857 84383
82796 79766 81454 10095 38837 86360 95068 00642 25125 20511
73929 84896 08412 84886 26945 60424 19652 85022 21066 11863
06744 27862 20391 94945 04712 37137 86960 95636 43719 17287
46776 46575 73962 41389 08658 32645 99581 33904 78027 59009
```

Figure 29

From a table of π to 10,000 decimals, calculated on the IBM 704 by Cie IBM, France, Institut de Calcul Scientifique. Limited space does not permit the presentation of the entire table.

Four thousand decimals of π

```
94657 64078 95126 94683 98352 59570 98258 22620 52248 94077
26719 47826 84826 01476 99090 26401 36394 43745 53050 68203
49625 24517 49399 65143 14298 09190 65925 09372 21696 46151
57098 58387 41059 78859 59772 97549 89301 61753 92846 81382
68683 86894 27741 55991 85592 52459 53959 43104 99725 24680

84598 72736 44695 84865 38367 36222 62609 91246 08051 24388
43904 51244 13654 97627 80797 71569 14359 97700 12961 60894
41694 86855 58484 06353 42207 22258 28488 64815 84560 28506
01684 27394 52267 46767 88952 52138 52254 99546 66727 82398
64565 96116 35488 62305 77456 49803 55936 34568 17432 41125

15076 06947 94510 96596 09402 52288 79710 89314 56691 36867
22874 89405 60101 50330 86179 28680 92087 47609 17824 93858
90097 14909 67598 52613 65549 78189 31297 84821 68299 89487
22658 80485 75640 14270 47755 51323 79641 45152 37462 34364
54285 84447 95265 86782 10511 41354 73573 95231 13427 16610

21359 69536 23144 29524 84937 18711 01457 65403 59027 99344
03742 00731 05785 39062 19838 74478 08478 48968 33214 45713
86875 19435 06430 21845 31910 48481 00537 06146 80674 91927
81911 97939 95206 14196 63428 75444 06437 45123 71819 21799
98391 01591 95618 14675 14269 12397 48940 90718 64942 31961

56794 52080 95146 55022 52316 03881 93014 20937 62137 85595
66389 37787 08303 90697 92077 34672 21825 62599 66150 14215
03068 03844 77345 49202 60541 46659 25201 49744 28507 32518
66600 21324 34088 19071 04863 31734 64965 14539 05796 26856
10055 08106 65879 69981 63574 73638 40525 71459 10289 70641

40110 97120 62804 39039 75951 56771 57700 42033 78699 36007
23055 87631 76359 42187 31251 47120 53292 81918 26186 12586
73215 79198 41484 88291 64470 60957 52706 95722 09175 67116
72291 09816 90915 28017 35067 12748 58322 28718 35209 35396
57251 21083 57915 13698 82091 44421 00675 10334 67110 31412

67111 36990 86585 16398 31501 97016 51511 68517 14376 57618
35155 65088 49099 89859 98238 73455 28331 63550 76479 18535
89322 61854 89632 13293 30898 57064 20467 52590 70915 48141
65498 59461 63718 02709 81994 30992 44889 57571 28289 05923
23326 09729 97120 94433 57326 54893 82391 19325 97463 66730

58360 41428 13883 03203 82490 37589 85243 74417 02913 27656
18093 77344 40307 07469 21120 19130 20330 38019 76211 01100
44929 32151 60842 44485 96376 69838 95228 68478 31235 52658
21314 49576 85726 24334 41893 03968 64262 43410 77322 69780
28073 18915 44110 10446 82325 27162 01052 65227 21116 60396
```

Figure 29 (cont.)

If the digits were divided absolutely evenly there would be 200 of each so it is clear that after 2,000 digits no particular digit is running a strong favorite. The problem awaits final solution for it is a theoretical one and cannot be resolved by such computations.

The direct scientific usefulness of the 10,000-place answer is practically zero. The indirect benefits are considerable. When a new automatic computing machine has been designed and constructed and before it is placed in day to day operation, it must be tried out to see whether its components are functioning properly. Moreover a staff of coders and programmers who are skilled in mathematics must be trained in the proper formulation of machine instructions. The computation of π offers an opportunity to test out a machine or to train personnel with a problem that has a long history and tradition. The mysterious and wonderful π is reduced to a gargle that helps computing machines clear their throats. No doubt also, long computations appeal to people who like to set records.

George Mallory was asked in 1922 why he attempted Mount Everest. "It was there," he answered. π is there and has been for a long time, and although its computation to 10,000 decimals is these days somewhat like getting to the top of Mount Everest in a helicopter, there are enough difficulties present to make it interesting. There is always the chance something may be learned, if not at the destination, perhaps on the journey.

Problem Set 18

1. Prove that Liouville's number is not a fraction and is not normal.

2. Carry the analysis given for π on pp. 69–70 to 4,000 digits.

3. *Poker and Pi.* It is possible to play poker with the digits in π. Think of the groups of five numbers on pp. 72–73 as constituting a poker hand. Thus, if you received 14159, you would have a pair of 1's. The order of the digits doesn't count. If you received 52552, you would have a full house (three of a kind plus a pair). Now if the digits of π occur in a random fashion, as one supposes they do, and if one looks at a vast number of poker hands made up in this way, we should obtain very nearly the following theoretical distribution of hands

Busts	29.52 %
One Pair	50.40 %
Two Pairs	10.80 %
Three of a Kind	7.20 %
Full House	.90 %
Straight	.72 %
Four of a Kind	.45 %
Five of a Kind	.01 %
Total	100.00 %.

These percentages were obtained by determining exactly what fraction of the 100,000 possible poker hands made up of the ten digits fall into each category. They are different for poker played with cards.

Determine the actual distribution of the 400 hands listed on page 72 and compare with the predicted values.

Statisticians use this "Poker Test" to establish randomness.

19. Back Over the Trail

In this section, some of the details that were left out in telling the π story will be filled in. We will take up: (a) Estimating π by Geometry, (b) The Crescent of Hippocrates, (c) Computing with Infinite Series, (d) Repeating Decimals, and (e) Squaring the Circle. Not all of this bears on large numbers or long numbers as such, but it will round out our understanding of the ideas mentioned.

(a) *Estimating π by Geometry.* Draw a circle whose diameter is one unit in length. Draw a square *PQRS* with its sides touching the circle. This is a *circumscribed square*. Draw a second square *TUVW* contained in the circle with its vertices on the circumference. This is an *inscribed square*. Figure 30 shows the circle and both squares.

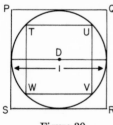
Figure 30

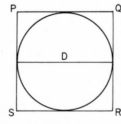
Figure 31

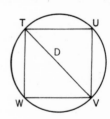
Figure 32

It is intuitively clear that the perimeter of the inner square is less than the length of the circumference of the circle and this in turn is less than the perimeter of the outer square. Let us express this in symbols. Let C designate the circumference of the circle, and $\overline{PQRS}$ the perimeter of the outer square and $\overline{TUVW}$ the perimeter of the inner square. Then

$$\overline{TUVW} < C < \overline{PQRS}.$$

Let D designate the diameter of the circle. Divide every term of this inequality by D. Then

$$\frac{\overline{TUVW}}{D} < \frac{C}{D} < \frac{\overline{PQRS}}{D}.$$

Notice that the quantity C/D is the definition of π. Therefore we can write

$$\frac{\overline{TUVW}}{D} < \pi < \frac{\overline{PQRS}}{D}$$

and so we have π shut in between two other numbers whose value we shall now compute.

Since $PQRS$ is a square the length $\overline{PQRS}$ is $4 \times$ the length $\overline{PQ}$. Notice also from Figure 31 that $\overline{PQ} = D$ so that

$$\frac{\overline{PQRS}}{D} = \frac{4 \times \overline{PQ}}{D} = \frac{4 \times D}{D} = 4.$$

To obtain the second ratio, we can proceed as follows, see Figure 32. The triangle TWV has a right angle at W. Pythagoras' theorem tells us that

$$\overline{TW}^2 + \overline{WV}^2 = \overline{TV}^2 = D^2.$$

But $\overline{TW} = \overline{WV}$ and so

$$\overline{TW}^2 + \overline{TW}^2 = D^2 \quad \text{or} \quad 2\overline{TW}^2 = D^2.$$

This means that

$$\overline{TW}^2 = \frac{D^2}{2} \quad \text{and} \quad \overline{TW} = \frac{D}{\sqrt{2}}.$$

Thus,

$$\overline{TUVW} = 4 \times \overline{TW} = \frac{4}{\sqrt{2}} D.$$

Hence,

$$\frac{\overline{TUVW}}{D} = \frac{4}{\sqrt{2}} = 2\sqrt{2} \, .$$

If we now combine this information, we have

$$2\sqrt{2} < \pi < 4 \, .$$

In decimals,

$$2.828 \ldots < \pi < 4.000 \ldots \, .$$

This is a crude, but an easily obtained estimate.

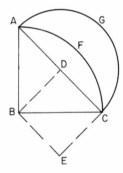

Figure 33. The crescent of Hippocrates

(b) *The Crescent of Hippocrates.* A modified statement of Hippocrates' discovery is this: Let ABC be a triangle with a right angle at B and two equal sides AB and BC. D is the midpoint of AC. With B as a center and AB as radius, draw the arc of the circle AFC. With D as center and AD as radius, draw the semicircle AGC. Construct the square $BDCE$. The area of the crescent $AGCFA$ is exactly equal to the area of the square $BDCE$. In this way the crescent is squared!

Here is a proof. The semicircle $ACGA$ has the same area as the quadrant $ABCFA$. For, the area of the quadrant is $\frac{1}{4} \times \pi \overline{AB}^2$. The area of the semicircle is $\frac{1}{2}\pi\overline{DC}^2$. But $\overline{DC} = \frac{1}{2}\overline{AC}$ and $\overline{AC} = \overline{AB}\sqrt{2}$. Therefore the area of the semicircle is $\frac{1}{2}\pi(\frac{1}{2}\sqrt{2}\,\overline{AB})^2 = \frac{1}{4}\pi\overline{AB}^2$. If you take the piece $ADCFA$ away from the semicircle, you get the crescent $AFCGA$. But if it is taken from the quadrant, you get the triangle ABC. This means that the area of the triangle ABC equals the area of the crescent. Finally, the triangle BEC is congruent to ABD so that the area of the square $BDCE$ equals the area of ABC equals the area of the crescent $AFCGA$.

(c) *Computing with Infinite Series*. Summing an infinite series approximately is very much like ordinary addition, but there are several differences. The numbers should be expressed in decimal form, and rounded to a certain number of figures. It would become increasingly difficult to carry out the arithmetic in fractional form. As more and more terms are added, the sum should "settle down," or converge, to the required answer. We cannot, of course, add *all* the terms together for there are an unlimited number of them. But we must add enough of them to make sure that the terms we have neglected will not affect the sum we compute, at least to the accuracy that we have chosen to compute it. It may be difficult to tell in advance how many terms to take. The subject is complicated by the fact that many infinite series are *divergent*, that is to say, when more and more terms are added, the sum does not settle down. For computation, we must have a *convergent* series, and preferably one which settles down with great rapidity.

As the first example, let us sum the series

$$1 + \frac{2}{5} + \frac{3}{5^2} + \frac{4}{5^3} + \frac{5}{5^4} + \frac{6}{5^5} + \frac{7}{5^6} + \ldots$$

The exact answer is known to be $\frac{25}{16}$ or 1.5625.

$1 = 1.00000000$	Sum of 1 term	1.00000000
$\frac{2}{5} = .40000000$	Sum of 2 terms	1.40000000
$\frac{3}{5^2} = \frac{3}{25} = .12000000$	Sum of 3 terms	1.52000000
$\frac{4}{5^3} = \frac{4}{125} = .03200000$	Sum of 4 terms	1.55200000
$\frac{5}{5^4} = \frac{5}{625} = .00800000$	Sum of 5 terms	1.56000000
$\frac{6}{5^5} = \frac{6}{3,125} = .00192000$	Sum of 6 terms	1.56192000
$\frac{7}{5^6} = \frac{7}{15,625} = .00044800$	Sum of 7 terms	1.56236800
$\frac{8}{5^7} = \frac{8}{78,125} = .00010240$	Sum of 8 terms	1.56247040
$\frac{9}{5^8} = \frac{9}{390,625} = .00002304$	Sum of 9 terms	1.56249344
$\frac{10}{5^9} = \frac{10}{1,953,125} = .00000512$	Sum of 10 terms	1.56249856.

After ten terms have been added, we are quite close to the correct answer; our error is less than .0000015. For more accuracy, we would have to take additional terms.

As a final example, we shall sum Machin's series for π. The convergence of this series is quite rapid and this has made it a favorite with computers.

$$\pi = \frac{16}{5} - \frac{16}{3 \times 5^3} + \frac{16}{5 \times 5^5} - \frac{16}{7 \times 5^7} + \frac{16}{9 \times 5^9} - \frac{16}{11 \times 5^{11}} + \cdots$$

$$- \frac{4}{239} + \frac{4}{3 \times 239^3} - \frac{4}{5 \times 239^5} + \frac{4}{7 \times 239^7} - \cdots$$

Working to 10 decimals, we have:

$$\frac{16}{5} = \qquad 3.2000000000$$

$$\frac{-16}{375} = -0.0426666667$$

$$\frac{16}{15,625} = \qquad 0.0010240000$$

$$\frac{-16}{546,875} = -0.0000292571$$

$$\frac{16}{17,578,125} = \qquad 0.0000009102$$

$$\frac{-16}{537,109,375} = -0.0000000299$$

$$\frac{16}{15,869,140,625} = \qquad 0.0000000010$$

$$\frac{-4}{239} = -0.0167364017$$

$$\frac{4}{40,955,757} = \qquad 0.0000000977$$

Total: 3.1415926535 .

(d) *Repeating Decimals.* Repeating decimals can be handled by means of geometric series, but there is an arithmetic trick which enables us to do as much. Suppose we would like to find the value of the repeating decimal .36363636 . . . . Write

$$r = \quad .3636363636 \ldots,$$

then $\qquad 100r = 36.3636363636 \ldots.$

Subtract the first equation from the second,

$$99r = 36.0000000 \ldots = 36 .$$

Thus
$$r = \frac{36}{99} = \frac{4}{11} .$$

Sometimes a repeating decimal has an initial portion which does not repeat. For instance, .2314314314314 . . . . Such decimals can be treated in the same way. Write

$$r = \quad .23143143143143 \ldots ,$$

then
$$1000r = 231.43143143143143 \ldots$$
$$r = \quad .23143143143143 \ldots$$

Subtract:
$$999r = 231.20000000 \ldots = 231.2$$

$$r = \frac{231.2}{999} = \frac{2312}{9990} = \frac{1156}{4995} .$$

In this way, it can be shown that any repeating decimal is equivalent to a fraction.

The reverse is true: Every fraction, when expressed as a decimal either "comes out even" or repeats indefinitely. It is not difficult to see the reason for this if you examine a sample division. Suppose that $1/7$ is converted to a decimal. Follow the division process.

```
        .1428571
    7 )1.0000000
        7
        30
        28
        20
        14
        60
        56
        40
        35
        50
        49
        10
        7
        30
```

As soon as we hit the remainder of 1 in the subtraction we are back where we started and the whole process must repeat itself over and over again without end.

The same must be true when any division is carried out. If a is divided by b to form a/b, certain remainders will be found. In the example above, the remainders are 1, 3, 2, 6, 4, 5, 1, ... One then brings down the zero and divides again. The remainders must all be less than the denominator b, otherwise the division is improperly performed. Therefore, only the numbers 1, 2, 3, 4, . . . up to $b - 1$ are possible remainders. We do not include 0, for if a zero turns up, the division comes out evenly. Since the number of different remainders possible is at most $b - 1$, a remainder must turn up after $b - 1$ or fewer divisions which has already appeared. When this occurs, the whole division process will repeat itself.

(e) *Squaring the Circle.* This is an activity which for thousands of years has been a spur to the wise and a pitfall to the ignorant. The problem is as follows: Given a circle, construct, using a straight-edge and a compass, either a line segment whose length equals the circumference of the circle or a square whose area equals that of the circle. One must make very precise what "constructing" means, what type of thing one is allowed to do with the straight-edge and compass. We cannot go into the details, but the type of procedure allowed will be suggested by the construction given below. One is not allowed, for instance, to take the circle, cut it out and roll it along a straight line and in this way measure the circumference. Under appropriate rules of the game, squaring the circle is impossible. Yet, approximate solutions are possible and can yield as much accuracy as desired.

One simple construction, see Figure 34, was discovered by Kochansky (see Problem 5 of Section 17).

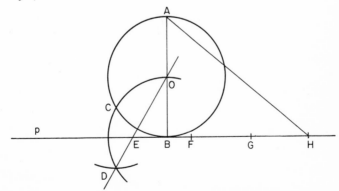

Figure 34. Kochansky's approximate quadrature of the circle.

π is approximated by $\sqrt{\dfrac{40}{3} - \sqrt{12}}$

Take a compass and draw a circle. Let O be its center. Keep the opening of the compass fixed throughout the construction. Let AB be a diameter. At B construct a line p that is perpendicular to AB. With B as a center, draw an arc which intersects the circle at C. With C as a center draw a second arc which intersects the first arc at D. Draw the line OD, intersecting the line p at E. With the compass, still using the same opening, measure off the equal lengths EF, FG and GH. Connect A and H. Then the length of AH is very nearly equal to the length of one half of the circumference of the circle.

This construction is equivalent to taking the value of π as 3.141533. This is an error of about .00006, or about 1 part in 16;000. It is doubtful that a construction with ruler and compass could actually be carried out with this much accuracy.

Problem Set 19

1. Change to repeating decimals: $\frac{1}{13}$, $\frac{1}{51}$, $\frac{1}{61}$.

2. Change the repeating decimal .246824682468 . . . to a fraction.

3. Change to a fraction: .196119611961 . . . .

20. The Personality of Numbers

In years gone by, a test of a good mathematician was whether he could handle large numbers. Three centuries ago, the two French mathematicians, Mersenne and Fermat, had a correspondence. Mersenne asked Fermat to factor the large number 100,895,598,169. Fermat wrote back that it equals $112,303 \times 898,423$ and that neither of these smaller numbers could be factored. It is an easy matter, requiring only a few minutes, to check that Fermat's multiplication is correct. It is vastly more difficult to arrive at this answer from scratch.

Today, only a relatively few mathematicians make this type of problem their principal concern. It is in the realm of *number theory*, a fascinating but exceedingly difficult branch of mathematics. Large numbers are of considerable importance to number theory and in this section we shall get an inkling of why this is so.

It appears that numbers, like men, have character. Just as there are tall men and fat men and cheerful men and honest men, there are even numbers and odd numbers and square numbers and prime numbers. Many special traits of numbers have been studied. Among the most important types of numbers there are:

Figure 35. The personality of numbers

Even Numbers: A number is *even* if it is divisible by 2.
Examples: 2, 4, 6, 8 .

Odd Numbers: A number is *odd* if it is not divisible by 2.
Examples: 1, 3, 5, 7 .

Square Numbers: A number is a *square* if it is the product of another number by itself.

Examples: $1 = 1^2$,　　$4 = 2^2$,　　$9 = 3^2$.

Cubes: A number is a *cube* if it is the third power of another number.

Examples: $1 = 1^3$,　　$8 = 2^3$,　　$27 = 3^3$.

Triangular Numbers: A number is *triangular* if it is the sum of consecutive integers beginning with 1.

Examples: $3 = 1 + 2$,　　$6 = 1 + 2 + 3$,　　$10 = 1 + 2 + 3 + 4$.

Prime Numbers: A number is *prime* if it is *not* the product of two numbers (other than itself and one).

Examples: 2, 3, 5, 7, 11, 1229.

Composite Numbers: A number is *composite* if it is the product of two numbers (other than itself and one).

Examples: $4 = 2 \times 2$,　　$6 = 2 \times 3$,　　$60 = 10 \times 6 = 2 \times 2 \times 3 \times 5$.

Perfect Numbers: A number is *perfect* if it is equal to the sum of all its divisors other than the number itself.

Example: 6; the divisors of 6 (other than 6 itself) are 1, 2 and 3.　　$6 = 1 + 2 + 3$,　　so 6 is a perfect number.

Some additional facts that characterize numbers will be found in the Table, "Who's Who Among the Integers," see pp. 92-93.

How does one find out what the personality of a number is? For low numbers this may be quite simple, but for large, complicated numbers, it may be very difficult. Sometimes simple tests can be developed.

Odds or Evens: This is simple. Merely look at the last digit of the number. If it is odd, the whole number is odd. If it is even, the whole number is even.

Squares: This is not so easy, especially if a large number is given. For the complete solution, extract the square root of the number. If it "comes out," the original number was a square, and its square root is automatically determined. There are partial tests which can sometimes be applied profitably. Notice that: $1 \times 1 = \underline{1}$, $2 \times 2 = \underline{4}$, $3 \times 3 = \underline{9}$, $4 \times 4 = 1\underline{6}$, $5 \times 5 = 2\underline{5}$, $6 \times 6 = 3\underline{6}$, $7 \times 7 = 4\underline{9}$, $8 \times 8 = 6\underline{4}$, $9 \times 9 = 8\underline{1}$, $10 \times 10 = 10\underline{0}$. If these facts are kept in mind, together with the process of multiplying a number by itself, we come to the following conclusion: a square must end in the digits 0, 1, 4, 5, 6, or 9. It cannot end in a 2, 3, 7, or 8. For this reason, we can say without batting an eyelash that the number

$$1,289,409,673,828$$

cannot be a square. The converse is not true. If a number ends in 0, 1, 4, 5, 6, or 9 it is not necessarily a square.

Another partial test is this: Add the digits of the number up. If the sum has several digits, add them up. In this way, reduce all the digits to one digit. If the number started with was a square, the answer will be 1, 4, 7, or 9. If the answer is 2, 3, 5, 6, or 8, the number was not a square.

EXAMPLE: $123,457 \times 123,457 = 15,241,630,849$.

Now $1 + 5 + 2 + 4 + 1 + 6 + 3 + 0 + 8 + 4 + 9 = 43$

and $4 + 3 = 7$

The answer 7 is admissible for a square.

On the other hand, you may obtain 1, 4, 7, or 9 and still not have a square.

EXAMPLE: 205, $2 + 0 + 5 = 7$. But 205 is not a square.

Cubes: There is no simple and complete criterion for cubes in terms of its digits. The first digit of a cube may be anything at all. One partial test is this: add the digits of the number up. If the sum has several digits add them up. Reduce in this way to one digit. If the number started with was a cube, the answer will be either 1, 8, or 9. If the answer obtained is 2, 3, 4, 5, 6, or 7, the number is not a cube.

EXAMPLE: $1961 \times 1961 \times 1961 = 7,541,066,681$

Now $7 + 5 + 4 + 1 + 0 + 6 + 6 + 6 + 8 + 1 = 44$

and $4 + 4 = 8$

The answer 8 is admissible for a cube.

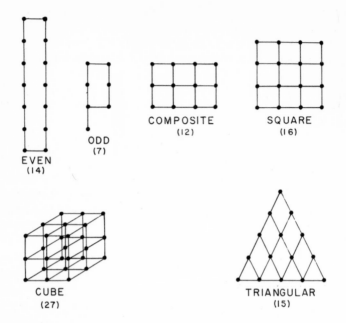

Figure 36. Some characteristics of numbers, exhibited geometrically

Triangular Numbers: A number N is a triangular number if and only if the number $8N + 1$ is a square. In this way, the problem is referred back to a corresponding problem for squares.

EXAMPLE: 28 is triangular and $8 \times 28 + 1 = 225$ is a square.

Composite Numbers and Prime Numbers: These terms are opposite. It is possible to give a simple test in terms of the digits for the divisibility of a number by a given divisor. The test depends upon what the divisor is.

Divisibility by 2: A number is divisible by 2 if and only if its last digit is divisible by 2.

Divisibility by 3: A number is divisible by 3 if and only if the sum of its digits is divisible by 3.

Divisibility by 4: A number is divisible by 4 if and only if its units' digit plus twice its tens' digit is divisible by 4.

Divisibility by 5: A number is divisible by 5 if and only if its units' digit is divisible by 5 (i.e., if it ends in 0 or 5).

Divisibility by 6: A number is divisible by 6 if and only if its units' digit is even and the sum of its digits is divisible by 3.

Divisibility by 7: A number is divisible by 7 if and only if 3 × units' digit + 2 × tens' digit − 1 × hundreds' digit − 3 × thousands' digit − 2 × ten thousands' digit + 1 × hundred thousands' digit is divisible by 7. If there are more digits present, the sequence of multipliers 3, 2, −1, −3, −2, 1 is repeated as often as necessary.

EXAMPLE: 7 × 457404 = 3,201,828

$$
\begin{array}{rcr}
3 \times 8 = & & 24 \\
2 \times 2 = & & 4 \\
-1 \times 8 = & & -8 \\
-3 \times 1 = & & -3 \\
-2 \times 0 = & & 0 \\
1 \times 2 = & & 2 \\
3 \times 3 = & & 9 \\
\hline
\text{Total:} & & 28
\end{array}
$$

(7 divides 28).

Divisibility by 8: A number is divisible by 8 if and only if its units' digit + 2 × tens' digit + 4 × hundreds' digit is divisible by 8.

Divisibility by 9: A number is divisible by 9 if and only if the sum of its digits is divisible by 9.

Divisibility by 10: A number is divisible by 10 if and only if its last digit is zero.

Divisibility by 11: A number is divisible by 11 if and only if its units' digit − its tens' digit + its hundreds' digit − its thousands' digit, etc. is divisible by 11.

Divisibility by 12: Test for divisibility by 4 and by 3.

Divisibility by 13: A number is divisible by 13 if and only if $10 \times$ units' digit $- 4 \times$ tens' digit $- 1 \times$ hundreds' digit $+ 3 \times$ thousands' digit $+ 4 \times$ ten thousands' digit $+ 1 \times$ hundred thousands' digit is divisible by 13. If there are more digits present, the sequence of multipliers $10, -4, -1, 3, 4, 1$ is repeated as often as necessary.

EXAMPLE: $13 \times 234,352,604 = 3,046,583,852$

$$
\begin{aligned}
10 \times 2 &= 20 \\
-4 \times 5 &= -20 \\
-1 \times 8 &= -8 \\
3 \times 3 &= 9 \\
4 \times 8 &= 32 \\
1 \times 5 &= 5 \\
10 \times 6 &= 60 \\
-4 \times 4 &= -16 \\
-1 \times 0 &= 0 \\
3 \times 3 &= 9 \\
\hline
\text{Total:} &\quad 91 \qquad (13 \text{ divides } 91)
\end{aligned}
$$

We illustrate the proof of these tests by demonstrating one case, that of three digit numbers and the divisor 7. Let N be a three digit number with digits a, b, and c. Then,

$$N = 100a + 10b + c .$$

Form the sum required by the test. Call it S:

$$S = -a + 2b + 3c .$$

Then, $$2S = -2a + 4b + 6c$$

and $$N + 2S = 98a + 14b + 7c = 7(14a + 2b + c) .$$

The sum $N + 2S$ is therefore a multiple of 7, say $7M$. Now if N is a multiple of 7, say $7P$, then $2S = 7M - 7P = 7(M - P)$, and it follows from this that S must also be divisible by 7. If, conversely, S is a multiple of 7, say $7Q$, then

$$N = 7M - 14Q = 7(M - 2Q) .$$

This tells us that N must be a multiple of 7.

Primes: To show that a number is a prime we must show that it is not divisible by 2, and not by 3, and not by 5, etc. Many divisions are involved. There is a way known as *Wilson's Theorem* which involves many multiplications but only one division. Wilson's Theorem states† that *a number N is a prime if and only if it divides the number*

$$1 \times 2 \times 3 \times 4 \times \ldots \times (N - 1) + 1 \, .$$

EXAMPLES:

$N = 2$	a prime	$N - 1 = 1$,	$1 + 1 = 2$,	
				2 divides 2 .
$N = 3$	a prime	$N - 1 = 2$,	$(1 \times 2) + 1 = 3$,	
				3 divides 3 .
$N = 4$	not a prime	$N - 1 = 3$,	$(1 \times 2 \times 3) + 1 = 7$,	
				4 does not divide 7 .
$N = 5$	a prime	$N - 1 = 4$,	$(1 \times 2 \times 3 \times 4) + 1 = 25$,	
				5 divides 25 .
$N = 6$	not a prime	$N - 1 = 5$,	$(1 \times 2 \times 3 \times 4 \times 5) + 1 = 121$,	
				6 does not divide 121 .
$N = 7$	a prime	$N - 1 = 6$,	$(1 \times 2 \times 3 \times 4 \times 5 \times 6) + 1 = 721$,	
				7 divides 721 .
$N = 8$	not a prime	$N - 1 = 7$,	$(1 \times 2 \times 3 \times 4 \times 5 \times 6 \times 7) + 1 = 5041$,	
				8 does not divide 5041 .

To carry out this test becomes increasingly difficult. It would be virtually impossible to test the number 4999 by this method and to verify that it is indeed a prime. The number you would have to compute is tremendous. Wilson's Theorem is of limited value in testing for primes.

Of the various characteristics of numbers, that of being prime is one of the most fascinating and one of the least predictable. The primes are scattered through the odd numbers in a highly irregular fashion. Here are the primes less than 100:

2, 3, 5, 7, 11, 13, 17, 19, 23, 29, 31, 37, 41,
43, 47, 53, 59, 61, 67, 71, 73, 79, 83, 89, 97 .

† For a proof of Wilson's Theorem, see *Elementary Number Theory* by J. V. Uspensky and M. A. Heaslet, McGraw-Hill, 1939, p. 153.

As we examine this list, we observe that the primes seem, on the average, to occur less and less frequently. In view of this, it is natural to ask whether there are only a finite number of them so that after a certain point all numbers may be factored. This cannot be true. *There are primes whose size is as large as you like.* The following proof given by Euclid (300 B.C.) is interesting for us because it is one of the few places that ancient mathematicians used large numbers in a theoretical argument.

Take a prime number, call it p. Now form the product of all the prime numbers up to p: $2 \times 3 \times 5 \times 7 \times \ldots \times p$. Thus, if you have selected $p = 7$, form the number $2 \times 3 \times 5 \times 7$. If you have selected $p = 19$, form the number

$$2 \times 3 \times 5 \times 7 \times 11 \times 13 \times 17 \times 19 .$$

Such a product is clearly larger than the prime number you have selected. To this product, add 1: $(2 \times 3 \times 5 \times \ldots \times p) + 1$. Give this sum the name N. Note that N is larger than p. Now then, there are two possibilities: either (a) N is a prime number or (b) N is not a prime number and hence is divisible by a prime. In case (a), we have found a prime number greater than p: N itself. We shall show that case (b) also leads to a prime number greater than p. When N is divided by 2 it goes $3 \times 5 \times \ldots \times p$ times, but leaves a remainder of 1. When N is divided by 3, it goes $2 \times 5 \times \ldots \times p$ times and leaves a remainder of 1. (Try these out with $p = 7$.) This is true for division by any of the numbers, 2, 3, 5, 7, 11, up to p. Hence N cannot be divided by any of the primes up to and including p. But we know that in case (b), N is divisible by some prime. It follows from this that there must be a prime number which is greater than p.

In either case (a) or case (b) we are led to the same conclusion: starting with a prime, p, we can find a prime which is larger than it. The list of the primes can never terminate.

As of 1960, the largest number known to be prime was $2^{3217} - 1$. There are primes that are larger but no one knows as yet which specific numbers they are!

Problem Set 20

1. Prove that 12,078,521,834 is not a square.
2. Show that 1,354,896 is a square.

3. Show that 5,601,816,576 is a cube.

4. Show that the product of two squares or of any number of squares is a square.

5. Same for cubes.

6. Show that if a square ends in an even integer, it must be divisible by 4.

7. Show that if a square ends in a 0, it must end in an even number of zeros.

8. Find the first number after 1 which is simultaneously a 1st power, a 2nd power, a 3rd power, a 4th power, a 5th power, a 6th power, a 7th power, an 8th power, a 9th power and a 10th power.

9. The year 1936 was a square. What is the next year that is square?

10. The year 1728 was a cube. What is the next year that is a cube?

11. Without performing any lengthy division, prove that the number 360,360 is divisible by all the integers from 2 to 13 inclusive.

12. Prove that this is the smallest positive number which is divisible in this manner.

13. The number 1001 is divisible by 7. So is the number 1000000001. Show that a number of the form 1000 . . . 0001 (where all the inside digits are zero) is divisible by 7, if and only if it has 2 zeros or 8 zeros or 14 zeros or 20 zeros, etc. The same thing is true for divisibility by 13.

14. A number is formed entirely of 1's. When is it divisible by 7 and when by 13?

15. Verify by Wilson's Theorem that 11 is a prime.

16. Every prime, other than 2 or 3, when divided by 6 must leave a remainder of 1 or 5.

17. Verify, but not by Wilson's Theorem, that 1951 and 1973 are prime numbers.

18. *An Unsolved Problem.* Notice that $2^2 + 1 = 5$ is a prime.
$$2^{2^2} + 1 = 17$$
is also a prime. Prove that
$$2^{2^{2^2}} + 1$$
is a prime. Is
$$2^{2^{2^{2^2}}} + 1$$
a prime? No one knows. It is a tremendous number.

Who's who among the integers
1–50

1 the unit, 1^n, triangular

2 prime, $1^n + 1^n$, the binary base

3 prime, triangular

4 2^2

5 prime, $1^2 + 2^2$

6 triangular, perfect, $1 \times 2 \times 3$

7 prime

8 2^3, $2^2 + 2^2$

9 3^2, $1^3 + 2^3$

10 2×5, $1^2 + 3^2$, triangular, decimal base

11 prime

12 $2^2 \times 3$

13 prime, $2^2 + 3^2$

14 2×7, $1^2 + 2^2 + 3^2$

15 3×5, triangular

16 4^2, 2^4, $2^3 + 2^3$

17 prime, $1^2 + 4^2$, $1^4 + 2^4$

18 2×3^2, $3^2 + 3^2$

19 prime

20 $2^2 \times 5$, $2^2 + 4^2$

21 3×7, triangular

22 2×11

23 prime

24 $2^3 \times 3$, $1 \times 2 \times 3 \times 4$

25 5^2, $3^2 + 4^2$

26 2×13, $1^2 + 5^2$

27 3^3

28 $2^2 \times 7$, triangular, perfect

29 prime, $2^2 + 5^2$

30 $2 \times 3 \times 5$, $1^2 + 2^2 + 3^2 + 4^2$

31 prime

32 2^5, $4^2 + 4^2$, $2^4 + 2^4$

33 3×11, $1^5 + 2^5$

34 2×17, $3^2 + 5^2$

35 5×7, $2^3 + 3^3$

36 $2^2 \times 3^2$, 6^2, $1^3 + 2^3 + 3^3$, triangular

37 prime, $1^2 + 6^2$

38 2×19

39 3×13

40 $2^3 \times 5$, $2^2 + 6^2$

41 prime, $4^2 + 5^2$

42 $2 \times 3 \times 7$

43 prime

44 $2^2 \times 11$

45 $3^2 \times 5$, $3^2 + 6^2$, triangular

46 2×23

47 prime

48 $2^4 \times 3$

49 7^2

50 2×5^2, $1^2 + 7^2$, $5^2 + 5^2$

51 3×17	77 7×11
52 $2^2 \times 13$, $4^2 + 6^2$	78 $2 \times 3 \times 13$, triangular
53 prime, $2^2 + 7^2$	79 prime
54 2×3^3, $3^3 + 3^3$	80 $2^4 \times 5$, $4^2 + 8^2$
55 5×11, triangular, $1^2 + 2^2 + 3^2 + 4^2 + 5^2$	81 3^4, 9^2
	82 2×41, $1^2 + 9^2$, $1^4 + 3^4$
56 $2^3 \times 7$	83 prime
57 3×19	84 $2^2 \times 3 \times 7$
58 2×29, $3^2 + 7^2$	85 5×17, $2^2 + 9^2$, $6^2 + 7^2$
59 prime	86 2×43
60 $2^2 \times 3 \times 5$	87 3×29
61 prime, $5^2 + 6^2$	88 $2^3 \times 11$
62 2×31	89 prime, $5^2 + 8^2$
63 $3^2 \times 7$	90 $2 \times 3^2 \times 5$, $3^2 + 9^2$
64 2^6, 4^3, 8^2, $2^5 + 2^5$	91 7×13, $1^2 + 2^2 + 3^2 + 4^2 + 5^2 + 6^2$, $3^3 + 4^3$, triangular
65 5×13, $1^2 + 8^2$, $4^2 + 7^2$, $1^3 + 4^3$, $1^6 + 2^6$	
	92 $2^2 \times 23$
66 $2 \times 3 \times 11$, triangular	93 3×31
67 prime	94 2×47
68 $2^2 \times 17$, $2^2 + 8^2$	95 5×19
69 3×23	96 $2^5 \times 3$
70 $2 \times 5 \times 7$	97 prime, $4^2 + 9^2$, $2^4 + 3^4$
71 prime	98 2×7^2, $7^2 + 7^2$, $1^4 + 2^4 + 3^4$
72 $2^3 \times 3^2$, $6^2 + 6^2$, $2^3 + 4^3$	
73 prime, $3^2 + 8^2$	99 $3^2 \times 11$
74 2×37, $5^2 + 7^2$	100 $2^2 \times 5^2$, 10^2, $6^2 + 8^2$, $1^3 + 2^3 + 3^3 + 4^3$
75 3×5^2	
76 $2^2 \times 19$	

Problem Set 20 (cont.)

19. *A Number Character.* G. H. Hardy writes a charming story about the famous Indian mathematician Ramanujan (1887–1920). "He (i.e., Ramanujan) could remember the idiosyncrasies of numbers in an almost uncanny way. It was Littlewood who said that every positive integer was one of Ramanujan's personal friends. I remember going to see him once when he was lying ill in Putney. I had ridden in a taxi-cab No. 1729, and remarked that the number seemed to me rather a dull one, and that I hoped it was not an unfavorable omen. 'No,' he reflected, 'it is a very interesting number; it is the smallest number expressible as the sum of two cubes in two different ways.' "†

Verify Ramanujan's statement by:

  (a) Finding two sets of two cubes such that the members of each set add up to 1729.

  (b) Showing that no smaller number has this property.

20. Prove the statement on page 86 about triangular numbers.

21. Casting Out Nines; The Number Theory of Residues

We shall study in detail one particular characteristic of numbers, their remainders upon division by 9. It is an extension of the notion of odds and evens. In former days it was taught in elementary school under the name of "the rule of nine" or "casting out nines" as a means of checking arithmetic. Though somewhat in abeyance as a mode of checking, it remains today as a source of amusement, the basis of many number tricks involving large numbers, and a fine introduction to a part of number theory known as the *theory of residues.*

When is a number even; when is it odd? A number is even if it is twice another number. It is odd if it is one more than an even number. We can express this algebraically:

$$\text{even number} = 2m$$

$$\text{odd number} = 2m + 1 .$$

The "other number" here is m. There is an alternate way of phrasing this: An even number has a remainder *zero* when divided by 2; an

---

† *Ramanujan*, Cambridge, 1940.

odd number has a remainder *one* when divided by 2. These remainders are known as *residues*. Upon division by two there are two possible residues, 0 and 1. On division by three there are three possible residues, 0, 1, and 2. On division by 7 the residues are 0, 1, 2, 3, 4, 5, 6. The general rule is this: on division by a number n there are n possible remainders or residues: 0, 1, . . . , $n - 1$.

Now just as all numbers can be classified into odds or evens, they can be classified according to their residues upon division by a given number. As an example, a number is either

(a) a multiple of 3 (i.e., 3 times another number).

(b) one more than a multiple of 3.

(c) two more than a multiple of 3.

These three classes correspond to residues of 0, 1, and 2 respectively upon division by 3. The classes (a), (b), (c) can be represented algebraically by:

$$\text{(a')} \ 3m \qquad \text{(b')} \ 3m + 1 \qquad \text{(c')} \ 3m + 2 .$$

We are going to pay exclusive attention to 9 as a divisor. Nine turns out to be quite an unusual divisor and has special properties because it is one less than 10, the number base. Upon division by 9 the nine possible remainders are 0, 1, 2, 3, 4, 5, 6, 7, and 8. These correspond algebraically to the expressions $9m$, $9m + 1$, $9m + 2$, $9m + 3$, $9m + 4$, $9m + 5$, $9m + 6$, $9m + 7$, and $9m + 8$. We can find the residue of any number by dividing it by 9 and seeing what is left over. What is the residue of 106,937?

```
           11881
        ---------
     9 ) 106937
           9
         ----
          16
           9
         ----
          79
          72
         ----
          73
          72
         ----
          17
           9
          ---
           8
```

The residue is 8.

The classification of all numbers according to their remainders upon division by 9 is illustrated by this diagram:

Residue class or remainder on division by 9	0	1	2	3	4	5	6	7	8
Algebraic form of number	$9m$	$9m+1$	$9m+2$	$9m+3$	$9m+4$	$9m+5$	$9m+6$	$9m+7$	$9m+8$
m									
0	0	1	2	3	4	5	6	7	8
1	9	10	11	12	13	14	15	16	17
2	18	19	20	21	22	23	24	25	26
3	27	28	29	30	31	32	33	34	35
4	36	37	38	39	40	41	42	43	44
5	45	46	47	48	49	50	51	52	53

Figure 37. The residue classes corresponding to 9 as divisor

It should be clear from this table that every number falls into a certain *residue class*, and in each class there are many numbers. Thus, the numbers 4, 13, 22, 31, . . . all comprise the residue class "4."

The residue of a number is part of its character. We shall use a special notation for it. If n is a given number we shall write $r(n)$ to mean the residue of n. Thus,

$$r(10) = 1, \qquad r(106{,}937) = 8, \qquad r(10 + 10) = 2 .$$

Note also that we can form residues of residues, thus

$$r[r(15) + r(16)] = r(6 + 7) = r(13) = 4 .$$

Residues satisfy three important laws:

FIRST LAW OF RESIDUES: *The residue of the sum of two numbers is equal to the sum of the residues of the individual numbers, with the proviso that if the last sum is greater than 8, we use its residue instead.*

EXAMPLE (a): $22 + 100 = 122$.

$$r(22) = 4 , \quad r(100) = 1$$
$$r(122) = 5 .$$

Therefore $\quad\quad\quad\quad r(22) + r(100) = r(22 + 100)$.

EXAMPLE (b): $15 + 16 = 31$

$$r(15) = 6 , \quad r(16) = 7 , \quad r(31) = 4$$

Since $6 + 7$ is greater than 8, we use its residue.

$$r(6 + 7) = 4 .$$

Thus $\quad\quad\quad\quad r(15 + 16) = r[r(15) + r(16)]$.

This law can be proved in the following way. Take any two numbers. Call them A and B. Write them algebraically exhibiting a division by 9. Thus, 9 goes into A a certain number of times, say m times, plus a remainder. 9 goes into B a certain number of times, say n, plus a remainder:

$$A = 9m + \text{a remainder}$$
$$B = 9n + \text{a remainder} .$$

These two remainders are precisely the residues, so we can write

$$A = 9m + r(A)$$
$$B = 9n + r(B) .$$

Adding these two equations,

$$A + B = 9m + r(A) + 9n + r(B)$$
$$= 9(m + n) + r(A) + r(B) .$$

Now, what happens when $A + B$ is divided by 9? It depends on how large $r(A) + r(B)$ is. Each number $r(A)$ and $r(B)$ is between 0 and 8. Therefore their sum is between 0 and 16. Suppose first $r(A) + r(B)$ is between 0 and 8. Then when

$$A + B = 9(m + n) + r(A) + r(B)$$

is divided by 9, it must go exactly $(m + n)$ times and leave over a remainder of $r(A) + r(B)$. But what is left over is precisely the residue of $A + B$. Thus, in this case

$$r(A + B) = r(A) + r(B) .$$

But suppose that $r(A) + r(B)$ happens to be between 9 and 16. Then we can write $r(A) + r(B) = 9 + r[r(A) + r(B)]$. Therefore

$$A + B = 9(m + n) + 9 + r[r(A) + r(B)] \, .$$

When 9 is divided into $A + B$ it will go precisely $(m + n) + 1$ times and leave a remainder of $r[r(A) + r(B)]$. In this case, therefore,

$$r(A + B) = r[r(A) + r(B)] \, .$$

This law can be extended to the sum of several numbers. As an example: $15 + 16 + 17 + 18 = 66$;

$$r(15) = 6 \, , \quad r(16) = 7 \, , \quad r(17) = 8 \, , \quad r(18) = 0 \, , \quad r(66) = 3 \, ;$$
$$r(6 + 7 + 8 + 0) = r(21) = 3 \, .$$

Therefore,

$$r(15 + 16 + 17 + 18) = r[r(15) + r(16) + r(17) + r(18)] \, .$$

SECOND LAW OF RESIDUES: *The residue of the product of two numbers is equal to the product of the residues of the individual numbers, with the proviso that if the last product is greater than 8, we take its residue instead.*

EXAMPLE (a): $2 \times 39 = 78$
$$r(2) = 2 \, , \quad r(39) = 3 \, , \quad r(78) = 6 \, .$$
$$r(2 \times 39) = r(2) \times r(39) \, .$$

EXAMPLE (b): $21 \times 39 = 819$
$$r(21) = 3 \, , \quad r(39) = 3 \, , \quad r(819) = 0 \, .$$

Since 3×3 is greater than 8, we use its residue instead.

Thus, $r(21 \times 39) = r[r(21) \times r(39)] = 0 \, .$

To prove this, proceed as before and let the two numbers be A and B. Write

$$A = 9m + r(A)$$
$$B = 9n + r(B) \, .$$

$$A \times B = [9m + r(A)] \times [9n + r(B)]$$
$$= 81m \times n \times 9n \times r(A) + 9m \times r(B) + r(A) \times r(B)$$
$$= 9[9m \times n + n \times r(A) + m \times r(B)] + r(A) \times r(B) \, .$$

There are now two possibilities.

First case: $r(A) \times r(B)$ is less than 9. Then, when $A \times B$ is divided by 9 it goes precisely $9m \times n + n \times r(A) + m \times r(B)$ times with $r(A) \times r(B)$ left over. In this case, then,

$$r(A \times B) = r(A) \times r(B) \ .$$

Second case: $r(A) \times r(B)$ is between 9 and 64 inclusive. In this case, we can write

$$r(A) \times r(B) = 9p + r[r(A) \times r(B)] \ .$$

Hence upon division of $A \times B$ by 9 it will go exactly

$$9m \times n + n \times r(A) + m \times r(B) + p$$

times with an amount equal to $r[r(A) \times r(B)]$ left over. In this case, then,

$$r(A \times B) = r[r(A) \times r(B)] \ .$$

The third law of residues relates particularly to 9 and provides an easy way of obtaining the residue. One does not have to divide at all! The residue can be obtained by adding up the digits of the number.

THIRD LAW OF RESIDUES: *The residue of a number is equal to the sum of the individual digits in the number, with the proviso that if this sum exceeds 8, we replace it by its residue.*

EXAMPLE (a): $r(123) = 6$, $1 + 2 + 3 = 6$

EXAMPLE (b): $r(106937) = 8$, $1 + 0 + 6 + 9 + 3 + 7 = 26$
$$r(26) = 2 + 6 = 8 \ .$$

We shall show how this law can be proved when the number has five or fewer digits. The proof for any number at all is roughly the same. Suppose that the digits of a number N are $a, b, c, d,$ and e. According to the decimal system the number N itself then amounts to

$$N = 10{,}000a + 1{,}000b + 100c + 10d + e \ .$$

Let us call the sum of the digits s. We have

$$s = a + b + c + d + e \ .$$

Since a, b, c, d, e are all between 0 and 9, the sum s is between 0 and 45. Notice

$$N = 9999a + 999b + 99c + 9d + a + b + c + d + e$$
$$= 9(1111a + 111b + 11c + d) + s .$$

Since s is between 0 and 45 we can write $s = 9t + r(s)$ where $r(s)$ is now less than 9. Hence

$$N = 9(1111a + 111b + 11c + d) + 9t + r(s) .$$

When N is divided by 9 it goes exactly

$$1111a + 111b + 11c + d + t$$

times and leaves a remainder $r(s)$. Thus $r(N) = r(s)$. If s happens to be less than 9, then s equals its residue and so $r(N) = s$.

Suppose in particular that a number N is a multiple of 9. Then $r(N) = 0$. Thus, if s designates the sum of the digits of N, we have $r(s) = 0$. This means that s is a multiple of 9. Conversely, if $r(s) = 0$, then $r(N) = 0$ and N must be a multiple of 9. This proves the important fact: The sum of the digits of a number is a multiple of 9 if and only if the number itself is a multiple of 9.

EXAMPLES:

$$9 \times 12 = 108 \qquad 1 + 0 + 8 = 9$$
$$9 \times 652 = 5,868 \qquad 5 + 8 + 6 + 8 = 27 = 9 \times 3$$
$$2 + 7 = 9$$
$$9 \times 1,299 = 11,691 \qquad 1 + 1 + 6 + 9 + 1 = 18 = 9 \times 2$$
$$1 + 8 = 9$$

We can now explain how these theorems lead to a check for addition and multiplication. Take the example of addition:

927		18		9
94		13		4
308	Form digit sums:	11	Form digit sums:	2
118		10		1
4		4		4
1,451				20

Form digit sums: $1 + 4 + 5 + 1 = 11,$
$$1 + 1 = 2 \qquad 2 + 0 = 2$$

The number 2 which has been obtained in two ways is merely $r(1,451)$. If the sum is correct, both answers must agree. If, therefore, we do not obtain agreement the original sum must be wrong. Unfortunately, the test is not a complete test. Even if we obtain agreement, the answer may possibly be in error.

We can shorten the process somewhat by "casting out nines," i.e., by ignoring all nines in sums, and when we exceed a nine, reducing the amount by 9.

927	0
94	4
308	2
118	1
4	4
1,451	11
2	2 Check

Multiplication works in a similar way:

375	$3 + 7 + 5 = 15, \quad 1 + 5 = 6$
$\times 26$	$2 + 6 = 8$
2250	
750	$6 \times 8 = 48, \quad 4 + 8 = 12$
9750	$1 + 2 = \underline{3}$

$9 + 7 + 5 + 0 = 21$

$2 + 1 = \underline{3}$

This work reflects the fact that $r(9750) = 3$.

Problem Set 21

1. Check the sum:

12905
28072
9001
6214
7728
64020

by casting out nines.

2. Determine without division whether the number: 16920203020201 is a multiple of 9.

3. Two numbers have the identically same digits, but in a different order (for instance, 127936 and 712639). Show that they have the same remainder when divided by 9. Show that their difference is a multiple of 9.

4. A certain number (not zero) whose digits consist only of 0's and 1's is known to be a multiple of 9. Show that the number cannot be smaller than 111,111,111.

5. Form the following numbers:

$$7$$
$$77$$
$$777$$
$$7777$$
$$\cdot$$
$$\cdot$$
$$\cdot$$

Prove that every 9th term in this sequence of integers is a multiple of 9. Are there other multiples of 9 in the sequence?

6. What about the sequences?

6		2
66		25
666	and	252
6666		2525
$\cdot$		25252
$\cdot$		$\cdot$
$\cdot$		$\cdot$
		$\cdot$

7. *Lightning Calculation.* The German lightning calculator, Johann Dase (1824–1861) once multiplied 79,532,853 by 93,758,479 in his head in 54 seconds. Check the answer 7,456,879,327,810,587 by casting out nines.

8. Without multiplying out, find the missing digit *d* in the product: 123,456 × 789,123 = 97,42*d*,969,088.

9. The number 162,5*d*0,792, where *d* indicates a missing digit, is a multiple of 9. Find *d*.

10. The number 6*d*,*d*23 is a multiple of 9. The *dd* indicates that a single unknown digit is missing two times. Find *d*.

22. The Hardest of the Simple Problems

We have seen that modern computing equipment has been used to calculate π to 10,000 decimals. It would be a mistake, though, to think that the hard mathematical problems these machines handle consist largely of computing individual numbers to a great many places. In scientific computations which occupy a good fraction of the time of electronic machines, the great accuracy implied by 20 or 30 figures simply has no meaning. What is characteristic of scientific computation is that it requires many many small computations, with long numbers creeping into these computations by the back door.

The problem of numerical weather prediction comes to mind. Its object is this: to predict the weather by means of the known laws of physics. Many things must be taken into account: the velocity of the air, its temperature, its pressure, its humidity, its friction with the earth and with itself, the rotation of the earth. There is hardly a better problem to illustrate sheer magnitude of computations. This is a brand new kind of research which has been made possible by high speed computers. No one knows yet how successful it will be.

The many physical quantities are related to one another by what is known as a *differential equation*. To predict the weather, this equation must be solved. The weather here affects the weather one mile away. The weather at 30,000 feet affects the weather on the ground.

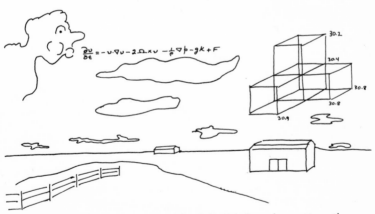

Figure 38. The wind and the rain. Scientists have been attempting to predict the weather by solving the equations of meteorology

It was found that, to make progress with the problem, the weather over a whole hemisphere of the earth must be considered simultaneously and information referring to about 50,000 places must be taken into consideration. Some of these places are on the ground and some are in the air up to a height of 10 miles. A twenty-four hour forecast may require as many as one billion multiplications, just to mention one type of arithmetic operation. With such a vast amount of arithmetic to perform, men and their slow ways are useless, but machines can perform them all in a reasonable amount of time. After all, we don't want to learn about tomorrow's weather two or three years from now.

In this chapter, we are going to take a look at a simple mathematical problem which arises with great frequency in science. The problem is that of solving a *system of simultaneous linear equations*. It is easy to tell a person how to go about solving such a problem. But he may find it very difficult to carry out the instructions. He may find that it is necessary to perform hundreds, perhaps thousands, of small arithmetic problems en route to the solution. He may find that his numbers, though small in the beginning, become incredibly large during the process of solution. This mathematical problem will then be related to a specific physical problem—that of determining the distribution of temperatures in a heated metal rod. In this way we shall get an inkling of how many numbers and large numbers, linear equations and differential equations all enter in the day to day work of a mathematician who deals with computation.

A single linear equation in one unknown quantity x looks, typically, like this

$$(1) \qquad\qquad 3x = 9 \ .$$

Three times a number x equals 9. The problem: find out what the number x is. The solution, as you can see is $x = 3$, and can be obtained by dividing both the left-hand side and the right-hand side of equation (1) by 3. The word "linear" comes from analytic geometry and means that the unknown quantity appears only in the first degree.

Sometimes such equations may appear in other forms. For instance,

$$(2) \qquad\qquad 2x - 6 = 3 - x \ .$$

But when all the like terms have been gathered together, we can write equation (2) in the form (1). We can consider the first form as a standard way of writing such equations.

A system of two linear equations in two unknowns may look like

(3)
$$\begin{cases} 3x + 4y = 13 \\ x - y = 2 . \end{cases}$$

The problem here is to find values of the two unknowns, x and y, which when inserted into each of these equations, make them both true. The brace { is sometimes placed near the equations and emphasizes that both equations are to be considered *simultaneously*, each with the other. The answer is $x = 3$, $y = 1$. This answer can be verified by trying it out:

$$(3 \times 3) + (4 \times 1) = 13$$
$$3 - 1 = 2 .$$

A system of 3 linear equations in 3 unknowns x, y, z, written in standard form, might look like this:

(4)
$$3x + 4y + 5z = 18$$
$$2x - y + 8z = 13$$
$$5x - 2y + 7z = 20 .$$

These lines mean that we are required to find numbers for $x, y,$ and z which make all 3 equations true simultaneously. The answer, as you can check, is $x = 3$, $y = 1$, $z = 1$.

We can keep this process up. We can write simultaneous equations in 4, 5, 6, 7 or any higher number of unknowns. We need as many equations as there are unknowns. The more unknowns the more space it takes to write down the system. Good abbreviations here might be very important, and this is one reason that the compound quantities known as matrices (see Section 3) were invented.

Systems of simultaneous equations express the interlocking relationships that may exist between various quantities. Two cans of plums and one can of peaches together cost $.99. One can of plums and two cans of peaches together cost $1.08. These two statements can be phrased mathematically. If a designates the cost (in pennies) of a can of plums and b designates the cost of a can of peaches then we have

(5)
$$2a + b = 99$$
$$a + 2b = 108 ,$$

two simultaneous linear equations in the two unknowns, a and b; from these we can determine what a and b are.

The world of nature and the world of men is full of interlocking relationships. A rainfall in the Ohio valley and a rainfall in the Missouri valley contribute to the level of the Mississippi River at Vicksburg, Mississippi in a certain way. A rise in the cost of steel and a rise in the cost of coal are reflected in the price of food. One of the jobs of a river engineer or an economist is to find out how.

We turn to a problem where the laws of interrelationship are pretty much known. Suppose that we have a long bar of iron. If one portion of the bar is heated, the heat will travel through the bar and warm up the portions that are cold. Think of a silver spoon placed in a cup of hot coffee. After a while, the bar comes into equilibrium with its surroundings and no longer continues to heat up. It maintains a steady distribution of temperatures throughout its entirety. It will be hottest where it is being heated and will be cooler as we move away from the source of the heat. Exactly how does the temperature change? This is an important problem.

In order to solve it we must know something about the laws of steady temperature. The law that applies here is that at every point inside a body, the steady temperature is the average of the temperatures at the surrounding points. This is an imprecise way of phrasing what is precisely done by means of the *differential equation of steady heat flow:*

(6) $$\frac{\partial^2 T}{\partial x^2} + \frac{\partial^2 T}{\partial y^2} = 0 \,.$$

We may call it the law of averages for temperature. Let us see what it means and how it works out.

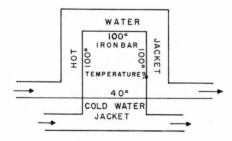

Figure 39. A boundary value problem of mathematical physics

Imagine the following situation. Our bar of iron, which we shall represent by a square, is surrounded on three sides by a jacket of hot water and on the fourth side by a jacket of cold water. The supply of hot water keeps the temperature of three edges at 100°F and the supply of cold water keeps the temperature of the fourth edge at 40°F. The heat flows through the bar and is drained off at the lower edge. How does the temperature of the bar vary in its interior?

We will apply the law of averages in this way. Divide the square into 9 smaller squares. Designate the points as marked and let the letters stand for the points as well as the temperature at these points. By the law of averages, the temperature at F is the average of the temperatures at surrounding points. Think of F as being "surrounded" by the four points of our grid closest to F; i.e., by E, B, G, and J. (See Fig. 40.)

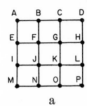
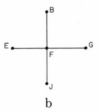

a   b

Figure 40

Now the average of 4 numbers is $\frac{1}{4}$ the sum of the numbers. This means that

$$(7) \qquad F = \tfrac{1}{4}(E + B + G + J) .$$

Eq. (7) is the interlocking relationship between the temperature at F and the temperature at the surrounding points. Now we can, and must write a similar equation for each interior point. For G we have

$$(8) \qquad G = \tfrac{1}{4}(F + C + H + K) .$$

For J we have

$$(9) \qquad J = \tfrac{1}{4}(I + F + K + N) .$$

And for K we have

$$(10) \qquad K = \tfrac{1}{4}(J + G + L + O) .$$

Now, some of the values are known from our experiment. All temperatures on the 3 upper edges are 100°. On the lower edge they are 40°. Thus, $I = E = B = C = H = L = 100$ and $N = O = 40$.

If we insert this information into the 4 equations (7), (8), (9), and (10) we can transform them into

(11) $$F = \tfrac{1}{4}(G + J + 200)$$

(12) $$G = \tfrac{1}{4}(F + K + 200)$$

(13) $$J = \tfrac{1}{4}(F + K + 140)$$

(14) $$K = \tfrac{1}{4}(G + J + 140).$$

These four relationships must hold simultaneously, and with a little bit of algebra, they may be converted into the standard form for simultaneous equations

(15)
$$\begin{aligned}
4F - G - J \quad\quad &= 200 \\
-F + 4G \quad\;\; - K &= 200 \\
-F \quad\quad + 4J - K &= 140 \\
- G - J + 4K &= 140.
\end{aligned}$$

The solution to this system of equations, as you can check, is

$$F = 92\tfrac{1}{2}, \quad G = 92\tfrac{1}{2}, \quad J = 77\tfrac{1}{2}, \quad K = 77\tfrac{1}{2}.$$

Though this is a correct answer to the system of equations designated by (15), it is only an approximate answer to the problem about the iron bar. The reason is not hard to find. We have assumed that the bar has only 4 interior points. There are many more points than that, and we should try to use as many as possible. The more we use the better our solution will be. We can divide our square into 16 smaller squares, see Fig. 41.

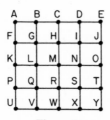

Figure 41

There will then be 9 interior points. At each of these points, the law of averages provides the interrelationship between the temperature at the point and the neighboring temperatures:

$$G = \tfrac{1}{4}(H + L + 200)$$
$$H = \tfrac{1}{4}(G + I + M + 100)$$
$$I = \tfrac{1}{4}(H + N + 200)$$
$$L = \tfrac{1}{4}(G + M + Q + 100)$$

(16)
$$M = \tfrac{1}{4}(L + H + N + R)$$
$$N = \tfrac{1}{4}(M + I + S + 100)$$
$$Q = \tfrac{1}{4}(L + R + 140)$$
$$R = \tfrac{1}{4}(Q + M + S + 40)$$
$$S = \tfrac{1}{4}(R + N + 140)$$

This is a system of 9 simultaneous equations in 9 unknowns, and we still have a fairly coarse subdivision of our square. To obtain a very accurate solution to our physical problem, we might have to introduce as many as 100 interior points and solve the resulting system of 100 equations in 100 unknowns.

Now that we have gained some insight into how simultaneous equations arise and why they are important, it is high time that we said a word about their solution. There are many different schemes for solving them. Perhaps several hundred. Some are very old and some are brand new. A common way is the *method of successive elimination*. In this method, by multiplying the equations appropriately and then subtracting them one from the other, we reduce the original system to another system which has one less unknown quantity. We proceed in this manner until we arrive at systems with . . . 3, 2, and finally 1 unknown quantity. An equation with one unknown, say $3x = 9$, is solved by dividing both sides by 3 to yield $x = 3$, and this, finally, gives us the numerical value of one of the unknown numbers. To find the others is now relatively easy. The process known as "back substitution" is used, and the numerical value of each additional variable is determined at the expense of solving one equation for each variable.

We will illustrate these vague directions by showing how to solve the system (4)

(4)
$$3x + 4y + 5z = 18$$
$$2x - y + 8z = 13 \qquad \text{original system}.$$
$$5x - 2y + 7z = 20$$

We will first eliminate the quantity x from this system. This can be done in two steps.

Step 1: Multiply the first equation by 2 and the second by 3. This will produce a $6x$ in each equation. Then subtract the two equations and the x will be eliminated:

$$6x + 8y + 10z = 36$$
$$6x - 3y + 24z = 39$$

$$\overline{ 11y - 14z = -3}$$

Step 2: Do the same thing for the first and third equations. Multiply the first by 5 and the third by 3. This will produce a $15x$ in each equation which will be eliminated upon subtraction:

$$15x + 20y + 25z = 90$$
$$15x - 6y + 21z = 60$$

$$\overline{ 26y + 4z = 30}$$

The two equations which do not contain x together constitute a reduced system:

$$11y - 14z = -3$$
$$26y + 4z = 30$$ 1st reduced system .

This reduced system contains no x. We now eliminate the y from this system. This is accomplished in one step.

Step 3: Multiply the first equation by 26, the second by 11 and subtract:

$$286y - 364z = -78$$
$$286y + 44z = 330$$

$$\overline{ - 408z = -408}$$

This leaves a single equation with only one unknown:

$$-408z = -408 \qquad \text{2nd reduced system .}$$

Step 4: Divide both sides of this equation by -408:

$$z = 1 .$$

Thus, we have determined the value of one unknown. Now comes the backward substitution.

Step 5: Substitute this value of z in the first equation of the first reduced system and solve it for y:

$$11y - 14 = -3$$
$$11y \qquad = 14 - 3 = 11$$
$$y \qquad = 1 \,.$$

We now know what y and z are.

Step 6: Substitute the known values of y and z in the first equation of the original system and solve for the x:

$$3x + 4 + 5 = 18$$
$$3x \qquad\quad = 18 - 9 = 9$$
$$x \qquad\quad = 3 \,.$$

We now have $x = 3$, $y = 1$, $z = 1$. This completes the solution of the problem. The answer may be checked, if desired, by substituting all the values, $x = 3$, $y = 1$, $z = 1$, in the second and third equations of the original system:

$$6 - 1 + 8 = 13 \qquad \text{check;}$$
$$15 - 2 + 7 = 20 \qquad \text{check.}$$

This, then, is the method of elimination. There is considerable work to it. Though some simplification can be introduced here and there, the solution above gives a fair idea of the amount of work necessary. The method is straightforward and systematic, yet until about 15 years ago when electronic computers were invented it was so difficult to solve such equations that many problems in physics and engineering and other parts of science simply could not be and were not solved. In the old days a man who solved a system of ten equations in ten unknowns was putting in a hard day's labor. A solution of 20 equations in 20 unknowns was a phenomenal achievement in computation, and virtually unknown. This was true, although mathematicians knew practically everything that needed to be known theoretically about such equations. The situation was so bad that physicists joked about the mathematicians saying that they knew everything about how to solve the problem but they couldn't actually do it.

What stood in the way? Two things did. Large systems lead to many numbers and to large numbers. In the problem just worked out, we performed 28 multiplications or divisions and 13 additions or subtractions to arrive at our answer. As more and more unknowns enter a problem the amount of work "snowballs." To solve a system with 10 unknowns we have to reduce it to a system with 9 unknowns, then to one with 8 unknowns, and so on down to 3, 2, and finally 1 unknown. If the letter N designates the number of unknown quantities that are involved in a system of linear equations then it has been shown that its solution requires approximately

$$\tfrac{1}{3}N^3$$

multiplications or divisions. We won't even bother to count the additions or subtractions. This means that if one were confronted with a system of 100 equations in 100 unknowns, it would require approximately

$$\tfrac{1}{3}(100)^3$$

or one third of a million multiplications or divisions to determine the answer. If a skilled computer using a small desk calculator were able to perform and record a multiplication in 30 seconds, it would take about

$$\tfrac{1}{3}(100)^3 \times \tfrac{1}{2} \times \tfrac{1}{60} \times \tfrac{1}{24} = 115.7$$

days just to perform the multiplications.

How do large numbers enter the problem? Probably the best way to understand this is by working out a larger system and seeing what happens. Take the system of 4 equations in 4 unknowns:

$$7x - 8y - 9z + 11w = 1$$
$$8x + 9y - 11z + 7w = 13$$
$$9x + 11y - 7z - 8w = 5$$
$$11x + 7y - 8z - 9w = 1 .$$

The numbers that appear in the equation are not very large. The solution is $x = 1$, $y = 1$, $z = 1$, $w = 1$, numbers which are also not large. We can verify that these numbers are the solution by inserting them in the equations. We now begin the elimination process.

$$56x - 64y - 72z + 88w = 8$$
$$56x + 63y - 77z + 49w = 91$$

$$-127y + 5z + 39w = -83$$

$$63x - 72y - 81z + 99w = 9$$
$$63x + 77y - 49z - 56w = 35$$

$$-149y - 32z + 155w = -26$$

$$77x - 88y - 99z + 121w = 11$$
$$77x + 49y - 56z - 63w = 7$$

$$-137y - 43z + 184w = 4$$

$$-127y + 5z + 39w = -83$$
$$-149y - 32z + 155w = -26 \qquad \text{1st reduced system}$$
$$-137y - 43z + 184w = 4$$

$$-18{,}923y + 745z + 5{,}811w = -12{,}367$$
$$-18{,}923y - 4{,}064z + 19{,}685w = - 3{,}302$$

$$4{,}809z - 13{,}874w = - 9{,}065$$

$$-17{,}399y + 685z + 5{,}343w = -11{,}371$$
$$-17{,}399y - 5{,}461z + 23{,}368w = 508$$

$$6{,}146z - 18{,}025w = -11{,}879$$

$$4{,}809z - 13{,}874w = - 9{,}065$$
$$6{,}146z - 18{,}025w = -11{,}879 \qquad \text{2nd reduced system}$$

$$29{,}556{,}114z - 85{,}269{,}604w = -55{,}713{,}490$$
$$29{,}556{,}114z - 86{,}682{,}225w = -57{,}126{,}111$$

$$1{,}412{,}621w = 1{,}412{,}621 \qquad \text{3rd reduced system}$$

Finally: $w = 1$.

We will not pursue the backward substitution to determine the remaining unknowns. If you examine this process, you will notice that to arrive at the first reduced system we multiply the numbers of the original system. To arrive at the second reduced system we multiply the numbers of the first reduced system. Thus, if the numbers of the original system are one digit long, those of the first reduced system will be about 2 digits long. Those of the second reduced system will be about 4 digits long, those of the third about 8 digits long. Each elimination may multiply by 2 the number of digits we have to carry. If we were faced with solving a system of 100 equations in one hundred unknowns, involving one or two digit numbers, we might be compelled to deal finally with numbers that have 2^{99} digits in them. This is a tremendous number of digits, and practically speaking it is impossible to do. It cannot be done when computing by hand, or even with an electronic computer. A way out must be found. The way out is a compromise. Only a fixed number of digits is retained: the most important or significant digits. The rest are thrown away. They are simply ignored. This naturally results in error, a kind of error known as *round-off*. Depending upon the case, round-off may be negligible or it may be serious, so serious in fact that the computations carried out may be worthless.

In electronic computers today systems of 100 equations are commonplace and can be run through in a matter of minutes. Systems of 1000 equations are less frequent and may occupy several hours of calculating time. These computations are carried out with about 8 or 10 decimals. For more accuracy the number of decimals carried may be doubled or tripled. But the added time required to compute with these extra length numbers is considerable.

Large numbers and plenty of them. Grist for the mill of electronic machinery. Then, round-off error. It may be very difficult to tell how accurate the answers are that the machines put out. Tremendous progress has been made. But a linear system of equations still remains the most difficult of the simple problems.

Problem Set 22

1. Solve the system (5).
2. Solve the system

$$6x \quad -y + \quad z = 8$$
$$x + \ 5y \quad -z = 7$$
$$3x - \ 8y + \ 4z = 3 \ .$$

3. Try to solve the system

$$6x \quad -y+ \quad z = \quad 8$$
$$x+ \quad 5y \quad -z = \quad 7$$
$$8x+ \quad 9y \quad -z = 10 .$$

What seems to be the trouble?

4. Solve the system (16). It will simplify matters considerably if you note that the answer must be symmetric about the axis CW. That is to say, in the answer we must have $G = I$, $L = N$, $Q = S$. Why should this be the case?

23. Infinities Beyond Infinity: The Growth of Sequences

Up to now we have given our attention to single numbers, to numbers considered as individuals. There is another vantage point from which numbers may be regarded. We may consider a succession of numbers and observe the tendency of the succession as a whole. This will bring us to the notion of growth. Growth is a universal phenomenon. Depress the accelerator of a car and its speed will increase. Place $10 in a savings bank, do not touch the account, and your balance will grow. The population of the United States grows; so does a colony of yeast cells in a brewer's vat. The universe itself is growing. Things are always in a state of growth, of decline, of change, and it is only natural that mathematics should have developed some ideas to reflect this.

The sequence of integers

$$1 , 2 , 3 , 4 , 5 , 6 , 7 , 8 , 9 , 10 , \ldots$$

expresses a situation of constant and uniform growth. Think of the drip, drip, drip of a faucet into a wash basin. The integers grow steadily, and by the relentless addition of sufficiently many 1's can be made to exceed any magnitude. The amount of growth from number to number is found by subtracting two adjacent numbers. Thus,

Sequence:	1	2	3	4	5	6	7	8	9	10 ...
Growth, or Difference:		1	1	1	1	1	1	1	1	1 ...

The growth here is constant. There are many sequences which show constant growth. For instance,

$$
\begin{array}{lcccccc}
\text{Sequence:} & 3 & 7 & 11 & 15 & 19 & 23 \ldots \\
\text{Growth, or} & & & & & & \\
\text{Difference:} & 4 & 4 & 4 & 4 & 4 \ldots
\end{array}
$$

or

$$
\begin{array}{lccccc}
\text{Sequence:} & 10 & 10\tfrac{1}{2} & 11 & 11\tfrac{1}{2} & 12 \ldots \\
\text{Difference:} & \tfrac{1}{2} & \tfrac{1}{2} & \tfrac{1}{2} & \tfrac{1}{2} \ldots
\end{array}
$$

A sequence of numbers that has constant growth is known as an *arithmetic sequence*. All such sequences can be made to exceed any given number.

Not all sequences of numbers have constant growth however. Take a look at the squares:

$$
\begin{array}{lccccc}
\text{Original Sequence:} & 1 & 4 & 9 & 16 & 25 \ldots \\
\text{Growth, or Difference:} & 3 & 5 & 7 & 9 \ldots
\end{array}
$$

Note that the growth is not constant; the growth itself is growing. But the growth of the growth is constant.

$$
\begin{array}{lcccc}
\text{Growth or Difference:} & 3 & 5 & 7 & 9 \ldots \\
\text{Growth of Growth or} & & & & \\
\text{Second Difference:} & 2 & 2 & 2 \ldots
\end{array}
$$

The squares form a sequence which grows faster than the integers or indeed, faster than the terms of any arithmetic sequence. The growth of 1, 4, 9, 16, . . . is more rapid than that of 1, 2, 3, 4, . . . for another reason. If we divide the corresponding terms of the first sequence by those of the second sequence, the ratios are:

$$
\frac{1}{1}, \frac{4}{2}, \frac{9}{3}, \frac{16}{4}, \ldots
$$

or

$$
1, 2, 3, 4, \ldots
$$

In other words the sequence of squares grows so fast with respect to the sequence of integers that the ratio of their respective sizes becomes larger and larger.

Let us see what happens when we take the sequence of cubes:

Original Sequence: 1   8   27   64   125   216 . . .
Growth, or Difference: 7   19   37   61   91 . . .
Growth of Growth, or
2nd Difference: 12   18   24   30 . . .
Growth of Growth of
Growth, or 3rd Difference: 6   6   6 . . .

It appears that the sequence of cubes grows so rapidly that not only do its differences grow, but its second differences grow steadily also. The third differences, however, are steady. The cubes grow faster than either the integers or the squares. This will be revealed by taking ratios:

$$\frac{\text{Cubes}}{\text{Integers}}: \quad \frac{1}{1}, \frac{8}{2}, \frac{27}{3}, \frac{64}{4}, \ldots \quad \text{or} \quad 1, 4, 9, 16, \ldots$$

$$\frac{\text{Cubes}}{\text{Squares}}: \quad \frac{1}{1}, \frac{8}{4}, \frac{27}{9}, \frac{64}{16}, \ldots \quad \text{or} \quad 1, 2, 3, 4, \ldots.$$

The general rule can now be guessed. For instance, if we start with 4th powers, then the first differences, 2nd differences, 3rd differences all grow in size but the 4th differences will be constant. The sequence of 4th powers grows more rapidly than the sequence of 1st, 2nd, or 3rd powers. The sequence of 10th powers grows extremely rapidly.

For squares, this growth can be depicted geometrically, as in Figure 42. Think of a square that is growing in size. When the side is small, only a small amount of area is added. But when the side is already large, the growth is large.

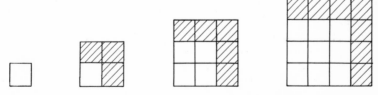

Figure 42. Growth of squares

It should be clear from this diagram that the growth is almost equal to twice the length of the side. It is exactly one less than twice the side. The ratio of the growth to the side of the square is almost two and becomes more and more nearly two as the square grows larger. We can illustrate this numerically by making a table:

Length of side	Area	Growth of area	Growth of area / Length of side
1	1	–	–
2	4	3	$3/2 = 1.5000$
3	9	5	$5/3 \approx 1.6666$
4	16	7	$7/4 = 1.7500$
5	25	9	$9/5 = 1.8000$
6	36	11	$11/6 \approx 1.8333$
.	.	.	.
.	.	.	.
10	100	19	$19/10 = 1.9000$
.	.	.	.
.	.	.	.
100	10,000	199	$199/100 = 1.9900$
.	.	.	.
.	.	.	.
1000	1,000,000	1999	$1999/1000 = 1.9990$

You can show in the same way that the growth of a cube is roughly proportional to its surface area. The general fact is this. The growth of a sequence of nth powers is roughly proportional to the $n - 1$st powers.

A sequence of numbers which becomes steadily larger and which can be made to exceed any magnitude whatever is called a *scale of growth*. We have seen how to make scales of growth corresponding to each integer. We need merely take the sequence of appropriate powers. Such scales are called *power scales*.

Power scale no.	Scale of growth
1	1 2 3 4 5 6 ...
2	1^2 2^2 3^2 4^2 5^2 6^2 ...
3	1^3 2^3 3^3 4^3 5^3 6^3 ...
4	1^4 2^4 3^4 4^4 5^4 6^4 ...
.	.
.	.
.	.

Figure 43. The power scale of growth

INFINITIES BEYOND INFINITY

Just as 5 is greater than 4, 3, 2, or 1, the scale of 5th powers grows more rapidly than that of any smaller power. The scale of 20th powers is of more rapid growth than the scale of 10th powers.

Now you may wonder, is it possible to devise a scale which grows more rapidly than that of the 100th power, of the 1000th power, of the 10^6 power; a scale which, in fact, grows so rapidly that its growth exceeds that of any power whatever? The answer is yes. And surprising though this fact may be, such a scale is not difficult to find. The successive powers of two form such a scale. Why is this so? Notice first what happens when we form the differences:

Powers of Two	1	2	4	8	16	32	64 . . .
First Difference		1	2	4	8	16	32 . . .
Second Difference			1	2	4	8	16 . . .
Third Difference				1	2	4	8 . . .

The growth of the original sequence is the same sequence over again! This means that when we form successive differences we come back to the powers over and over again. None of the growths—as opposed to the case of power scales—ever stops growing. Note also this fact: The growth of this sequence is proportional to the sequence itself.

Term of sequence	Growth	$\dfrac{\text{Growth}}{\text{Term}}$
1	–	–
2	1	$\frac{1}{2} = .5$
4	2	$\frac{2}{4} = .5$
8	4	$\frac{4}{8} = .5$
16	8	$\frac{8}{16} = .5$
32	16	$\frac{16}{32} = .5$

Figure 44. Powers of 2

In the previous case, the growth was proportional to something less than the original sequence. Sequences whose growth is proportional to the sequence itself are known as *geometric or exponential sequences*. The difference between a power sequence and an exponential sequence, when written out, is that in the former, the power is fixed and in the latter, the quantity raised to the power is fixed, and the power itself increases.

Suppose we would like to show by taking ratios that the scale 1, 2, 4, 8, 16, . . . grows more rapidly than, say, the 100th power scale. This scale is 1^{100}, 2^{100}, 3^{100}, 4^{100}, ... At first sight, this seems impossible to believe. After all, 2^{100}, the second term of the power scale is a tremendous number, far greater than 2, the 2nd number of the exponential scale. 3^{100} is even more tremendous and far greater than 4. None the less, let us mark down the ratios:

$$\frac{2^0}{1^{100}}, \frac{2^1}{2^{100}}, \frac{2^2}{3^{100}}, \frac{2^3}{4^{100}}, \frac{2^4}{5^{100}}, \frac{2^5}{6^{100}}, \frac{2^6}{7^{100}}, \frac{2^7}{8^{100}}, \frac{2^8}{9^{100}}, \frac{2^9}{10^{100}}, \cdots$$

Notice what is happening. The numerators in the terms (after the first term) in the beginning of this sequence are decidedly smaller than the denominators. The fractions are tiny. But the numerators are doubling with each term. The denominators are also increasing, it is true, but it is a bit difficult to see how fast. Can the numerators actually catch up with and overtake the denominators?

We shall show that they can. It may take quite a few steps, but eventually that is what happens. In order to make this convincing, we will first prove an inequality that relates to powers and which will help us to simplify some approximate computations. We shall prove that if p represents a positive quantity and if n is an integer greater than 1, then

$$(1 + p)^n > 1 + np .$$

This says, for instance, that

$$(1 + p)^2 > 1 + 2p \quad \text{or} \quad (1 + p)^8 > 1 + 8p$$

and so on. It can be proved as follows:

$$(1 + p)^2 = 1 + 2p + p^2 .$$

Now p^2 is a positive quantity, hence $1 + 2p + p^2$ is greater than $1 + 2p$. Therefore

$$(1 + p)^2 > 1 + 2p .$$

This proves the inequality for $n = 2$. Now, multiply this last inequality by the positive quantity $1 + p$. We obtain

$$(1 + p)^2(1 + p) > (1 + 2p)(1 + p) .$$

Simplify this,

$$(1 + p)^3 > 1 + 3p + 2p^2 .$$

Since $2p^2$ is positive, $1 + 3p + 2p^2 > 1 + 3p$. Therefore

$$(1 + p)^3 > 1 + 3p .$$

Multiply once again by the positive quantity $1 + p$,

$$(1 + p)^3(1 + p) > (1 + 3p)(1 + p) .$$

Simplify,

$$(1 + p)^4 > 1 + 4p + 3p^2 .$$

Since $3p^2$ is positive $1 + 4p + 3p^2 > 1 + 4p$, and hence

$$(1 + p)^4 > 1 + 4p .$$

In this way, the inequality can be proved for any exponent n.

Let us now return to our ratios, and mark down some that occur quite far along in the sequence.

$$\frac{2^0}{1^{100}}, \frac{2^1}{2^{100}}, \frac{2^2}{3^{100}}, \ldots, \frac{2^9}{10^{100}}, \ldots, \frac{2^{99}}{(100)^{100}}, \ldots,$$

$$\frac{2^{999}}{(1000)^{100}}, \ldots, \frac{2^{9999}}{(10,000)^{100}}, \ldots.$$

The claim is now made that by the time the sequence has reached the quantity $\frac{2^{999}}{(1000)^{100}}$, the numerator has caught up with the denominator and the fraction is greater than 1. For,

$$\frac{2^{999}}{(1000)^{100}} = \frac{1}{2} \times \frac{2^{1000}}{(1000)^{100}} = \frac{1}{2} \times \frac{(2^{10})^{100}}{(1000)^{100}}$$

$$= \frac{1}{2} \times \frac{(1024)^{100}}{(1000)^{100}} = \frac{1}{2} \times \left(\frac{1024}{1000}\right)^{100}$$

$$= \frac{1}{2} (1.024)^{100} .$$

Now, select $p = .024$ and $n = 100$. Then, $np = 2.4$. By the inequality we just proved,

$$(1 + p)^n = (1.024)^{100} > 1 + 2.4 = 3.4 .$$

This means that

$$\tfrac{1}{2}(1.024)^{100} > \tfrac{1}{2}(3.4) = 1.7 .$$

The value of $2^{999}/(1000)^{100}$ is greater than 1.7. The numerator has indeed caught up with the denominator.

By going out further and further in the sequence, the ratio increases and can be made indefinitely large. Take the term $2^{9999}/(10{,}000)^{100}$, for instance. We may verify by the law of exponents that

$$\frac{2^{9999}}{(10{,}000)^{100}} = \frac{2^{8669} \times (2^{10})^{133}}{10 \times (1000)^{133}}.$$

Since $2^{10} = 1024$, this is

$$\frac{2^{8669}}{10} \times \left(\frac{1024}{1000}\right)^{133} = \frac{2^{8669}}{10} \times (1.024)^{133}.$$

Since $(1.024)^{133}$ is surely greater than 1, and 10 is less than 2^4, the original term is greater than 2^{8665}.

The scale $1, 2, 4, 8, \ldots$ grows faster than the scale of 100th powers. In the same way, we can show that it grows faster than the scale of 1,000,000th powers, or indeed, than that of any power whatever.

Now if we have assigned the number 1 as a scale number for the first power and 2 for the second power, etc., what number shall we assign to the scale $1, 2, 4, 8, \ldots$? It cannot be an integer for it grows more rapidly than any power scale. Its tag should be "larger" than any of these. It should be beyond the finite. We may speak of $1, 2, 4, 8, \ldots$ as being a *transfinite scale of growth* as far as the power scales are concerned.

The geometric scales are themselves of different growths. Thus,

Powers of 2: $2^0, 2^1, 2^2, 2^3, \ldots$

Powers of 3: $3^0, 3^1, 3^2, 3^3, \ldots$

The powers of 3 grow more rapidly than the powers of 2. Proof? Consider the ratios:

$$\frac{3^0}{2^0}, \frac{3^1}{2^1}, \frac{3^2}{2^2}, \frac{3^3}{2^3}, \ldots$$

These ratios equal

$$\left(\frac{3}{2}\right)^0, \left(\frac{3}{2}\right)^1, \left(\frac{3}{2}\right)^2, \left(\frac{3}{2}\right)^3, \ldots$$

or

$$(1.5)^0, (1.5)^1, (1.5)^2, (1.5)^3, \ldots$$

The general term is $(1 + \tfrac{1}{2})^n$. Now we know that

$$\left(1 + \frac{1}{2}\right)^n > 1 + \frac{n}{2}.$$

As n becomes larger and larger so does $n/2$ and hence also $(1.5)^n$. In this way, we can set up a second family of scales of increasing growth.

Exponential scale number	Scale of growth
2	2^0 2^1 2^2 2^3 2^4 $\ldots$
3	3^0 3^1 3^2 3^3 3^4 $\ldots$
4	4^0 4^1 4^2 4^3 4^4 $\ldots$
.	.
.	.
.	.

Figure 45. The exponential scales of growth

Each scale grows more rapidly than its predecessor and any of them grows more rapidly than those in Figure 43.

Can we obtain a scale which grows more rapidly than any exponential scale? Yes. The scale, formed by the sequence of numbers

$$1^1, 2^2, 3^3, 4^4, 5^5, 6^6, \ldots,$$

in which both the powers and the base increase, grows more rapidly than any exponential scale or any power scale. If we make the exponents of this last scale increase more rapidly than the integers, we shall have a scale of yet more rapid growth. Thus,

$$1^1, 2^4, 3^9, 4^{16}, 5^{25}, 6^{36}, \ldots.$$

There is no end to this. The situation is summed up by a mathematical theorem derived in the 1870's by Paul duBois-Reymond. If we are given *any* sequence of scales of growth, each of which is more rapid than its predecessor, it is possible to devise a scale whose growth is more rapid than all of these.

Scales of growth are sometimes referred to as *orders of infinity*. In this way, mathematics gives us not only infinities, but infinities beyond infinities, and infinities beyond those.

A GALLERY OF DISTINGUISHED SEQUENCES ARRANGED IN ORDER OF INCREASING RAPIDITY OF GROWTH

The Integers	The Prime Numbers	The Squares	The Cubes	The Fibonacci Numbers†	The Powers of 2	The Factorials	The Coupled Exponentials
n	p_n	n^2	n^3	F_n	2^n	$1 \times 2 \times 3 \times \cdots \times n$	n^n
1	2	1	1	1	2	1	1
2	3	4	8	2	4	2	4
3	5	9	27	3	8	6	27
4	7	16	64	5	16	24	256
5	11	25	125	8	32	120	3,125
6	13	36	216	13	64	720	46,656
7	17	49	343	21	128	5,040	823,543
8	19	64	512	34	256	40,320	16,777,216
9	23	81	729	55	512	362,880	387,420,489
10	29	100	1,000	89	1,024	3,628,800	10^{10}
100	541	10^4	10^6	‡5.7×10^{20}	‡$10^{30.1}$	‡9.346×10^{157}	10^{200}
1,000	7,919	10^6	10^9	‡7.02×10^{208}	‡10^{301}	‡4.02×10^{2567}	10^{3000}
10^{10}	‡2.3×10^{10}	10^{20}	10^{30}	‡$10^{2.09 \times 10^9}$	‡$10^{3.01 \times 10^9}$	‡$2.496 \times 10^{9.57 \times 10^{10}}$	$10^{10^{11}}$

† See Problem 8 of Problem Set 23   ‡ Approximate value

Problem Set 23

1. *The Race.* Consider two sequences (A) and (B). Sequence (A) starts at 100 and has constant growth of 1000 per number. Sequence (B) starts at 2 and triples with each number. How many steps does it require for (B) to catch up with (A)?

2. Form ratios and show that the scale $\sqrt{1}, \sqrt{2}, \sqrt{3}, \sqrt{4}, \ldots$ is of slower growth than 1, 2, 3, 4, ...

3. Show that the scale: $1\sqrt{1}, 2\sqrt{2}, 3\sqrt{3}, 4\sqrt{4}, \ldots$ is of more rapid growth than 1, 2, 3, . . . but is slower than $1^2, 2^2, 3^2, \ldots$.

4. Find a scale of growth more rapid than:

$$1, 2^2, 3^{3^3}, 4^{4^{4^4}}, \ldots .$$

5. *Family Tree.* Every person has 2 parents, 4 grandparents, and 8 great grandparents. What is the general rule for computing the number of ancestors a given number of generations removed?

6. *The Paradox of the Ancestors.* According to the rule developed in the last problem, how many ancestors 40 generations (about 1200 years) ago does a person have? What is wrong with the answer obtained?

7. The sequence 1, 1, 2, 2, 3, 3, 4, 4, . . . grows, but not steadily. See what happens to the successive differences.

8. The sequence of numbers 1, 2, 3, 5, 8, 13, 21, 34, 55, . . . is famous in mathematics and is known as the *Fibonacci sequence.* Each number (after the 2nd) is the sum of the two preceding numbers. For instance, $13 = 8 + 5$, $34 = 21 + 13$. What are the next three numbers in this sequence? Show that the growth of the sequence is the sequence itself. Hence infer that this sequence grows more rapidly than any power sequence. Show that this is not a geometric sequence. Although it is not strictly geometric it becomes more and more nearly so. Show that the ratio of successive terms, e.g., 8/5, 13/8, 21/13, etc. becomes closer and closer to

$$\frac{1 + \sqrt{5}}{2} = 1.618034 \ldots .$$

24. Atomic Numbers, Astronomical Numbers, and Where Is Man?

One final word. If we read in our newspaper "Outlay for Development Astronomical, says Congressman," we know that he is not talking about developments in outer space but about improvements on dear old mother earth. "Astronomical" is merely a synonym for "exceedingly large." It comes by this meaning honestly. Look at some of the figures that must be used to describe the universe. The distance from the earth to the sun is 9.3×10^6 miles. The speed of light is 1.9×10^5 miles per second. In one year light travels 6×10^{12} miles. This distance is known as a *light year* and is a unit of distance that is to an astronomer as perhaps an inch is to a surveyor. The distance to the nearest star outside our solar system is

$$4.3 \text{ light years} = 2.5 \times 10^{13} \text{ miles}.$$

The diameter of our galaxy is 100,000 light years. There are nebulae outside the Milky Way which are 1,000,000 light years $= 6 \times 10^{18}$ miles away.

Astronomers look outward in space, from man to the stars, from the stars to the galaxies. Physicists, chemists, and biochemists look inward from man to systems of molecules, from molecules to the fundamental particles of physics such as electrons, protons, positrons, neutrons, etc. Here the numbers are correspondingly small. Astronomically small, we might say. Atomically small would be more accurate. The diameter of a common bacterium is $1/25,000 = 4 \times 10^{-5}$ inches. The diameter of a hydrogen atom is

$$\frac{1}{250,000,000} = 4 \times 10^{-9} \text{ inches.}$$

The mass of an electron is 9.1×10^{-28} grams. These are some examples of small numbers in the universe.

Man seems to be half way between the atoms and the stars. Not in the sense of usual averages, but in the sense of proportion. Men who study the universe as a whole have made the observation that an atom is to a man as a man is to an average sun. We can write an equation for this:

$$\frac{\text{ATOM}}{\text{MAN}} = \frac{\text{MAN}}{\text{SUN}}.$$

Man is a *mean proportional* or the *geometric mean* between an atom and a sun.

Let us verify this equation for masses. The mass of the sun is 2×10^{33} grams. The mass of a 150 pound man is 6.8×10^4 grams. The mass of a hydrogen atom is 1.7×10^{-24} grams. Inserting these values in our equation we have

$$\frac{1.7 \times 10^{-24}}{6.8 \times 10^4} = \frac{6.8 \times 10^4}{2 \times 10^{33}}$$

or $2.5 \times 10^{-29} = 3.4 \times 10^{-29}$ which is correct to within an order of magnitude.

Five hundred years ago, in the days before the scientific revolution swept the world, man was at the center of the universe. His earth was fixed, and the sun, the moon, and the stars revolved about him. He was the principal inhabitant of the earth, a unique creation, and, at least in the western mind stood in a unique relation to his Creator. Man, poor fellow, was man-centered. The discoveries of the past five centuries have led scientists to reformulate man's position in the universe. He is the inhabitant of a small planet revolving about an average size sun located in a galaxy among millions of other galaxies. As a biological specimen, he is the end product of a long evolutionary process and related intimately with other forms of life. As a moral and ethical specimen he is constantly in trouble. As a manifestation of life, he and his fellow earth creatures are probably not unique. Astronomers have estimated that there are probably billions of celestial bodies that are capable of sustaining organic life.

This is the picture as of 1960. It is one which should destroy man's man-centeredness. Yet, scientists have provided us with the equation we have just verified. In a vastly different way, it again restores man to a central place. Midway between the stars and the atoms, he occupies a fortunate position. He can look both ways. He studies the large and the small and with soaring imagination has created mathematical theories that transcend them both.

Miscellaneous Problems

1. A number system based on 26 is used and the letters of the alphabet are the digits:

$A = 0$, $B = 1$, $C = 2$, $D = 3$, ..., $X = 23$, $Y = 24$, $Z = 25$.

In this system, which is larger, the number whose representation is *HUNDRED, THOUSAND,* or *MILLION?* In this system, how much is *ONE + ONE?*

2. *Russian Squash.* The following problem appeared in the "Olympiads," a mathematical test given to Russian students. Write a large number down. Call it *N*. Suppose it has *n* digits. Let *k* be another number less than *n*. It is proposed to strike out *k* of the digits of *N* in such a manner that the remaining digits, when squashed together form a number which is as large as possible. The problem is to devise a systematic way of doing this.

EXAMPLE: Take *N* = 2790581, then *n* = 7. Select *k* = 3. If we strike out 2, 0, and 1, 7958 is left. If we strike out 2, 7 and 9, 581 is left.

3. A piece of wire screen is woven twelve wires to the inch. A circle of diameter twenty inches is cut out of the screen. Approximately how many squares are in the piece? Approximately how many inches of wire are in it?

4. *Getting to the Queen in Four Shakes.* Have you ever shaken the hand of the Governor of your state? If not, perhaps you have shaken the hand of someone who has—the mayor of your town or some other distinguished citizen. In such a case, you shook the hand of the man who shook the hand of the Governor. The Governor has very likely shaken the hand of the President. The President has shaken the hand of the Queen of England. In this way, a chain of 4 hand shakes can be set up linking you with the Queen. See if you can get to (a) the President of the U.S., (b) Mahatma Gandhi, (c) Abraham Lincoln, (d) George Washington, (e) Peter Ilyitch Tchaikovsky in as few shakes as possible. What is the relevance of this question to large numbers?

5. The following puzzle was recently made the object of a boxtop contest:

P
PYP
PYRYP
PYRARYP
PYRAMARYP
PYRAMIMARYP
PYRAMIDIMARYP
PYRAMIDODIMARYP
PYRAMIDOFODIMARYP
PYRAMIDOFVFODIMARYP
PYRAMIDOFVAVFODIMARYP
PYRAMIDOFVALAVFODIMARYP
PYRAMIDOFVALULAVFODIMARYP
PYRAMIDOFVALUEULAVFODIMARYP
PYRAMIDOFVALUESEULAVFODIMARYP

In how many ways can you spell "Pyramid of Values" by moving from letter to letter horizontally or vertically, forward or backward?

6. *Twenty Questions.* Do you know how to play the popular game of "Twenty Questions"? What is the relevance of powers of 2 to this game?

7. The physicist Sir Arthur Eddington once wrote that the universe is made up of exactly $\frac{3}{2} \times 136 \times 2^{256}$ particles. This is Eddington's number. Suppose this to be true and play the game of "Twenty Questions" with the particles of the universe. Show that it should be theoretically possible to guess any particle with at most 264 questions.

8. *Dictionary.* This modification of twenty questions has recently been popular as a lunch time game in scientific laboratories. It is generally played on a blackboard. A person thinks of a single word. His opponents try to guess what it is by mentioning other words. The first person responds by telling whether the correct word precedes or follows the guessed word in the dictionary. On the basis of this information, the opponents formulate another guess. Success after ten guesses is considered good for this game. Try it out.

9. What is the final digit in the number 3^{1001}? What is the first digit?

10. Following the pattern of Appendix I, make a table which illustrates the relative *costs* of different items. You might include, for instance, the cost of a glass of water, of a college education, of the annual U.S. budget, etc.

APPENDIX I

Some Selected Magnitudes in Science and Mathematics

Length
(All lengths are in feet)

Wave length of cosmic rays	10^{-20}	Size of minute bacteria	10^{-6}
Wave length of gamma radiation	10^{-12}	Size of large bacteria	10^{-5}
Radius of hydrogen atom	1.74×10^{-10}	Wave length, infrared radiation	10^{-4}
Size of colloidal particles	10^{-10} to 10^{-8}	Size of pollen grains	10^{-4}
Wave length of X-rays	10^{-10}	Size of minute insects	10^{-3}
Size of viruses	3×10^{-8}	Size of small insects	10^{-2}
Limit of microscopic vision	10^{-7}	Wave length of microwaves	10^{-2} to 10^{2}
ultraviolet	10^{-6}	Length of small shrew	1.6×10^{-1}
violet	1.48×10^{-6}	Height of man	5.8
blue	1.57×10^{-6}	Wave length radiowaves	10^{1} to 10^{5}
Wave lengths of light green	1.74×10^{-6}	Height of large African elephant at shoulder	1.15×10^{1}
yellow	1.90×10^{-6}	Length of brontosaurus	7×10^{1}
orange	1.97×10^{-6}	Length of sulphur bottom whale	10^{2}
red	2.10×10^{-6}	Height of Statue of Liberty	1.51×10^{2}

Height of Niagara Falls	1.67×10^2
Height of "General Sherman," the giant sequoia	2.72×10^2
Height of Washington Monument	5.55×10^2
Length of side of Great Pyramid	7.55×10^2
Length of S. S. Queen Mary	1.02×10^3
Height of Upper Yosemite Falls	1.43×10^3
Height of Empire State Building	1.472×10^3
Height of Kukenaam Falls, British Guiana	2×10^3
Length of channel span, Golden Gate Suspension Bridge, San Francisco	4.2×10^3
Height of Mt. McKinley	2.03×10^4
Height of Mt. Everest	2.9×10^4
Length of Panama Canal	2.68×10^5
Length of Suez Canal	5.44×10^5
Air distance: New York—Los Angeles	1.30×10^7
Length of Mississippi-Missouri River	2.1×10^7
Diameter of White Dwarf stars	$1.4 \text{ to } 9 \times 10^7$
Diameter of earth	4.18×10^7
Wave length of macrowaves	10^8
Circumference of earth	1.32×10^8
Mean distance: earth—moon	1.261×10^9
Diameter of sun	4.567×10^9
Diameter of giant stars	$6.8 \times 10^{10} \text{ to } 4.6 \times 10^{11}$
Mean Distance: earth—sun	4.9×10^{11}
Length of longest observed comet	10^{12}
Diameter of super giant stars	$4.6 \times 10^{11} \text{ to } 9.1 \times 10^{12}$
One light year	3.10×10^{16}
Distance to nearest star beyond the sun	1.32×10^{17}
Distances of 20 brightest stars in sky	$1.3 \times 10^{17} \text{ to } 1.7 \times 10^{19}$
Distance of sun to center of galaxy	1.1×10^{21}
Diameter of Milky Way	3×10^{21}
Distances of extra-galactic nebulae	3.1×10^{22}
Radius of universe according to Einstein's cosmology	10^{26}

Mass

(All masses are in pounds)

Electron	2.006×10^{-30}
Hydrogen atom	3.663×10^{-27}
Man	1.5×10^2
Elephant	$8 \times 10^3 \text{ to } 1 \times 10^4$
Sulphur bottom whale	3×10^5
Earth's atmosphere	1.14×10^{19}
Earth	1.2×10^{25}
Jupiter	3.84×10^{27}
Sun	4×10^{30}
Stars	$10^{30} \text{ to } 10^{32}$
Milky Way	6×10^{41}
Mass of universe according to Einstein-Eddington	4×10^{52}

Time

(All times are given in seconds)

Mean life of pion, π^0	10^{-16}	Month (synodic)	2.55×10^6
Mean life of K meson, K^+	1.2×10^{-8}	Mean solar year	3.15569×10^7
Mean life of muon, μ^-	2.2×10^{-6}	Life of dog	3×10^8
Time required for one addition on IBM 7090	4.4×10^{-6}	Period of Jupiter	3.74×10^8
Time for one vibration of audible sound	5×10^{-5} to 6.25×10^{-2}	Life of man	2×10^9
		Life of giant turtle	3×10^9
Half life of polonium 214	10^{-4}	Period of Pluto	7.82×10^9
Period of 60 cycle alternating current	1.667×10^{-2}	Half life of radium 226	5.24×10^{10}
Minute	6×10^1	Half life of radiocarbon	1.77×10^{11}
Hour	3.6×10^3	Period of precession of earth	8.2×10^{11}
Nodal period of Vanguard I	8.04×10^3	Period of rotation of Milky Way	6×10^{15}
Day	8.64×10^4	Half life of uranium 238	1.42×10^{17}

Density

(All densities given in pounds per cubic foot)

Average density of matter in the whole universe	10^{-28}	Aluminum	1.69×10^2
Hydrogen under standard conditions	5.61×10^{-3}	The moon	2.098×10^2
Air under standard conditions	8.07×10^{-2}	The earth	3.447×10^2
Oxygen	8.92×10^{-2}	Iron	4.91×10^2
White pine	2.2 to 3.1×10^1	Silver	6.55×10^2
		Lead	7.08×10^2
Water	6.24×10^1	Gold	1.178×10^3
Ebony	6.9 to 8.3×10^1	Iridium	1.40×10^3
The sun	8.86×10^1	Companion star to Sirius	9.4×10^6

Velocity

(All velocities are in miles per hour)

Turtle	10^{-2}
Fast swimmer	4.01
Fast runner	2.17×10^1
Passenger liner	3.5×10^1
Fast race horse	4.23×10^1
Swift	6×10^1
Cheetah	7×10^1
Eagle	1.2×10^2
Fast train	1.35×10^2
Racing speed boat	1.4×10^2
Racing auto	4×10^2
Gas engine plane	5×10^2
Sound in air at standard temperature and pressure	7.42×10^2
Rotational velocity of earth at equator	1.04×10^3
Turbojet plane	1.1×10^3
Rocket engine plane	2×10^3
Artificial satellites	1.8×10^4
Escape velocity of rocket from earth	2.5×10^4
Velocity of sun through space	4.25×10^4
Average velocity of earth in orbit	6.66×10^4
Maximum observed space velocity of a star	1.3×10^6
Orbital velocity of hydrogen electron	4.7×10^6
Rate of expansion of outermost galaxies	4.3×10^8
Velocity of light	6.696×10^8

Chronology

(All times given in years from present)

Formation of atoms	5×10^9
Formation of stars	4×10^9
Formation of earth	3.25×10^9
Beginning of life on earth	10^9
Age of fishes	3×10^8
Age of reptiles	2×10^8
Age of dinosaurs	1.5×10^8
Age of mammals	7.5×10^7
Age of mammoths	10^6
Beginnings of man on earth	3×10^5
Historical man	6×10^3
Pythagoras	2.5×10^3
Newton	3×10^2
Einstein	5×10^1

Temperature

(All temperatures given in degrees Fahrenheit)

Absolute zero	-4.597×10^2
Melting point of helium	-4.57×10^2
Lowest recorded temperature on earth (Siberia)	-9.36×10^1
Freezing point of mercury	-4×10^1
Freezing point of water	3.2×10^1
Body temperature	9.86×10^1
Highest recorded temperature on earth in shade (Sahara Desert)	1.36×10^2
Boiling point of water	2.12×10^2
Boiling point of mercury	6.7×10^2
Interior of coal furnace	2.7×10^3
Melting point of iron	2.8×10^3
Temperature at center of earth	5×10^3
Tungsten lamp	5.2×10^3
Boiling point of iron	5.4×10^3
Surface of sun	10^4
Surface temperature of stars	5.5×10^4 to 6×10^4
Interior of hot stars	5.4×10^7
Temperature at center of atomic bomb explosion	2×10^8

Games and Probabilities

Total number of bridge hands	6.35×10^{11}
Probability that at least one player in a bridge game will receive a complete suit of cards	2.52 chances in 10^{11}
Probability that each of four players in a bridge game will receive a complete suit of cards	4.47 chances in 10^{28}
Total number of ways of arranging 52 cards in a deck	8.0658×10^{67}
Chance of a monkey typing Shakespeare's "Hamlet" by random selection of keys	1 chance in $35^{27,000} \approx 10^{40,000}$
Number of possible chess games is less than	$10^{10^{70.5}}$

Small Probabilities

Sufficiently rare events will not be observed. The following chances have been considered to constitute an unobservable event† :

On the human scale:	1 chance in 10^6
On the terrestrial scale:	1 chance in 10^{15}
On the cosmic scale	1 chance in 10^{50}
Absolute zero	1 chance in 10^{500}

Miscellaneous Large Numbers

Number of molecules in a cubic inch of the best vacuum obtainable	6×10^{11}
Number of stars in the Milky Way	10^{12}
Number of atoms in a man's breath	10^{21}
Number of stars in the universe	10^{22}
Number of molecules in a pint of water	1.89×10^{25}
Number of electrons, protons, and neutrons in the universe	10^{79}
One of the largest known prime numbers (1961)	$2^{3217} - 1 \approx 10^{968}$
Skewes' Number (reputed to be the largest number that has occurred in a mathematical proof)	$10^{10^{10^{34}}}$

† According to E. Borel.

$$2^{8217} - 1$$

2	591 17086	013 20262	777 62467	679 22441	530 94181	888 75531	254 27303
974 92316	187 40192	665 86362	086 20120	951 68004	834 06550	695 24173	319 41774
416 89509	238 80701	741 03777	095 97512	042 31306	662 40829	163 53517	952 31118
615 48622	656 04547	691 12759	584 87756	105 68757	931 19101	771 14088	262 52153
849 03583	040 11850	721 16424	747 46182	303 14713	983 40229	288 07454	567 79079
410 37288	235 82070	589 23510	684 33882	986 88861	665 86502	809 27692	080 33960
586 93087	905 00409	503 70987	590 21190	183 71991	620 99400	256 89351	131 36548
829 73911	265 67973	032 41986	517 25011	641 27035	097 05427	773 47797	234 98216
764 43446	668 38311	932 25400	996 48994	051 79024	162 40565	190 54483	690 80961
606 16257	430 42361	721 86333	941 58524	264 31208	737 26659	196 20617	535 35748
892 89459	962 91951	830 82621	860 85340	093 79328	394 20261	866 58614	250 32514
507 73096	274 23537	682 29386	494 07127	700 84607	712 42118	230 80804	139 29808
705 75047	138 25264	571 44837	937 11250	320 81826	126 56664	908 42516	994 53951
887 78961	365 02484	057 39378	594 59944	433 52311	882 80123	660 40626	246 86092
121 50349	937 58478	229 22371	443 39628	858 48593	821 57388	212 32393	687 04616
067 73629	093 15071						

Figure 46. $2^{3217} - 1$, one of the largest known primes

APPENDIX II

Weights, Measures, and Equivalents

TABLE OF EQUIVALENTS: LENGTH

	Inches	Feet	Yards	Miles	Centimeters	Meters
1 inch	1	0.083 333 3	0.027 777 8	0.000 015 782 8	2.540 005	0.025 400 05
1 foot	12	1	0.333 333	0.000 189 393 9	30.480 06	0.304 800 6
1 yard	36	3	1	0.000 568 182	91.440 18	0.914 401 8
1 mile	63,360	5,280	1,760	1	160,934.72	1,609.347 2
1 centimeter	0.393 7	0.032 808 33	0.010 936 111	0.000 006 213 699	1	0.01
1 meter	39.37	3.280 833	1.093 611 1	0.000 621 369 9	100	1

Table of Equivalents: Area

	Square inches	Square feet	Square yards	Acres	Square miles	Square centimeters	Square meters
1 sq. in.	1	0.006 944 44	0.000 771 605	0.000 000 159 423	0.000 000 000 249 1	6.451 626	0.000 645 162 6
1 sq. ft.	144	1	0.111 111 1	0.000 022 956 8	0.000 000 000 035 870 1	929.034 1	0.092 903 41
1 sq. yd.	1,296	9	1	0.000 206 612	0.000 000 322 831	8 361.307	0.836 130 7
1 acre	6,272,640	43,560	4,840	1	0.001 562 5	40,468,726	4,046.873
1 sq. mi.	4,014,489,600	27,878,400	3,097,600	640	1	25,899,984,703	2,589,998
1 sq. cm.	0.154 999 69	0.001 076 387	0.000 119 598 5	0.000 000 024 710 4	0.000 000 000 038 610 06	1	0.000 1
1 sq. mtr.	1,549.996 9	10.763 87	1.195 985	0.000 247 104	0.000 000 386 100 6	10,000	1

TABLE OF EQUIVALENTS: VOLUME

	Cubic inches	Cubic feet	Cubic yards	Cubic centimeters	Cubic meters
1 cu. in.	1	0.000 578 704	0.000 021 433 47	16.387 162	0.000 016 387 16
1 cu. ft.	1,728	1	0.037 037 0	28,317.016	0.028 317 016
1 cu. yd.	46,656	27	1	764,559.4	0.764 559 4
1 cu. cm.	0.061 023 38	0.000 035 314 45	0.000 001 307 94	1	0.000 001
1 cu. meter	61,023.38	35.314 45	1.307 942 8	1,000,000	1

TABLE OF EQUIVALENTS: LIQUID MEASURE

	Fluid ounces	Liquid pints	Liquid quarts	Gallons	Liters	Cubic inches	Cubic feet
1 fluid oz.	1	0.062 5	0.031 25	0.007 812 5	0.029 572 9	1.804 89	0.001 044 38
1 liquid pt.	16	1	0.5	0.125	0.473 166	28.875	0.016 710 1
1 liquid qt.	32	2	1	0.25	0.946 332	57.75	0.033 420 1
1 gallon	128	8	4	1	3.785 329	231	0.133 680 6
1 liter	33.814 8	2.113 42	1.056 71	0.264 178	1	61.025 1	0.035 315 4
1 cu. in.	0.554 113	0.034 632 0	0.017 316 0	0.004 329 00	0.016 386 7	1	0.000 578 703 7
1 cu. ft.	957.506 5	59.844 16	29.922 08	7.480 519 5	28.316 22	1,728	1

TABLE OF EQUIVALENTS: DRY MEASURE

	Dry quarts	Pecks	Bushels	Liters	Cubic inches	Cubic feet
1 dry qt.	1	0.125	0.031 25	1.101 197	67.200 625	0.038 889 25
1 peck	8	1	0.25	8.809 57	537.605	0.311 114
1 bushel	32	4	1	35.238 3	2,150.42	1.244 456
1 liter	.908 103	0.113 513	0.028 378	1	61.025 1	0.035 315 4
1 cu. in.	0.014 880 8	0.001 860 10	0.000 465 025	0.016 386 7	1	0.000 578 703 7
1 cu. ft.	25.714 047	3.214 255 8	0.803 563 95	28.316 22	1,728	1

TABLE OF EQUIVALENTS: MASS

	Ounces (avoirdupois)	Pounds (avoirdupois)	Tons	Kilograms
1 avoirdupois oz.	1	0.0625	0.000 031 25	0.028 349 53
1 avoirdupois lb.	16	1	0.000 5	0.453 592 427 7
1 ton	32,000	2,000	1	907.184 86
1 kilogram	35.273 957	2.204 622 34	0.001 102 311 2	1

APPENDIX III

Formulas for Measurement

Length

Circumference of a circle	$c = \pi d = 2\pi r$
Theorem of Pythagoras	$c^2 = a^2 + b^2$

Area

Rectangle	$A = bh$
Square	$A = b^2$
Triangle	$A = \frac{1}{2}bh$
Circle	$A = \pi r^2$
Surface of sphere	$A = 4\pi r^2$

Volume

Box	$V = bht$
Cube	$V = b^3$
Sphere	$V = \frac{4}{3}\pi r^3$

Answers to Selected Problems

Set 2 (page 7)

1. The man on the street hardly ever does arithmetic with temperatures. He merely compares them: 52° is colder than 83° etc. He is using them as ordinals. The weather bureau also uses them as cardinals as, for instance, when they are added and divided to obtain average temperatures.

Set 3 (page 10)

2. He travels 11 blocks north and 6 blocks south, 9 blocks east and 9 west. At the end of his walk he is $11 - 6 = 5$ blocks north and $9 - 9 = 0$ blocks east. (What we have done to solve this problem is to say that 6 blocks south $= -6$ blocks north etc.) The Drunken Sailor was actually suggested by a very important problem in applied mathematics known as "the problem of the random walk."

3. $1.414 \times 1.414 = 1.999396$ $2 - 1.999396 = 0.000604$
$1.4142 \times 1.4142 = 1.99996164$ $2 - 1.99996164 = 0.00003836$

Set 4 (page 17)

1. Sixteen quadrillion, three hundred seventy-five trillion, two hundred eighty-nine billion, one hundred eighty-two million, three hundred forty-three thousand, eight hundred ninety-two has 153 letters, 5 hyphens and 5 commas, altogether 163 symbols.

3. There are 9 positive one digit numbers $(1, \ldots, 9)$. There are 90 positive two digit numbers $(10, \ldots, 19, 20, \ldots, 29, \ldots, 90, \ldots, 99)$.

In general there are $\overbrace{90 \ldots 00}^{n-1 \text{ zeros}}$ positive n digit numbers.

4. 9, 171.

5. If one of the whole numbers has more digits than the other, this number is the larger. Otherwise, starting at the left, compare the digits in the same position in each number until they are unequal. The larger digit belongs to the larger number. That is, let $a = a_n a_{n-1} \ldots a_1$ and $b = b_n b_{n-1} \ldots b_1$ be the two numbers. If

$a_n = b_n$, $a_{n-1} = b_{n-1}$, $\ldots$, $a_{k+1} = b_{k+1}$, $a_k < b_k$, then $a < b$.

Thus $6 = 6$, $0 = 0$, $2 < 6$ and so $60291 < 60621$.

The eye and the mind can go through this rule in a flash. If the numbers are large and unpunctuated, say

10069000701000 and 1006090000700100 ,

more time is required.

6. 9,964,411,   1,144,699.

7. The largest is $322,110$, the smallest is $011223 = 11,223$. But this is not a conventional way of writing numbers. The zero must occur inside. So we place it where it causes the least damage: $101,223$.

8. Eight, eighteen, eleven, fifteen, five, four, fourteen, nine, nineteen, one, seven, seventeen, six, sixteen, ten, thirteen, three, twelve, twenty, two.

9. $LXXXVIII = 88$, $C = 100$. The first occupies more space than the second, but is smaller. With Arabic numerals, the integer that occupies the most space is always the largest!

10. $(X + X + I + I)(L + X + V - I) = D + C + L - X +$
$$D + C + L - X +$$
$$L + X + V - I$$
$$L + X + V - I$$

$$\overline{}$$
$$= DDCCLLLLVV - II$$
$$= DDCCCCVIII$$
$$= MCDVIII$$

11. If we use the duodecimal system, i.e., base 12, we have

one dozen $\quad = (1 \times 12) + (0 \times 1) = $ (in duodecimal) 10

one gross $\quad = (1 \times 12 \times 12) + (0 \times 12) + (0 \times 1) = $ (in duodecimal) 100

one great gross $= (1 \times 12 \times 12 \times 12) + (0 \times 12 \times 12) + (0 \times 12) + (0 \times 1)$
$\qquad\qquad = $ (in duodecimal) 1000

12. Folio: The page size of a book made up of printer's sheets folded into 2 leaves.

Quarto: The page size of a book made up of printer's sheets folded into 4 leaves.

Octavo: The page size of a book made up of printer's sheets folded into 8 leaves.

Sixteenmo: The page size of a book made up of printer's sheets folded into 16 leaves.

Thirty-twomo: The page size of a book made up of printer's sheets folded into 32 leaves.

This suggests the binary system.

13. Suppose we allow plates with the numbers 0, 01, 0063, etc. To make one million plates we need†

Number of Plates with	Using Numbers		Using Letters	
1 symbol	10	⎫	26	⎫
2 symbols	10×10	⎪	26×26	⎪
3 symbols	$10 \times 10 \times 10$	⎬	$26 \times 26 \times 26$	⎬
4 symbols	$10 \times 10 \times 10 \times 10$	⎪	$26 \times 26 \times 26 \times 26$	475,254
5 symbols	$10 \times 10 \times 10 \times 10 \times 10$	⎭ 111,110		524,746
6 symbols		888,890		
Total		1,000,000		1,000,000

If we use numbers, we need a plate large enough to carry 6 symbols. Using letters, we need only 5 symbols. Provided that letters and numbers are the same size and that all plates are made the same width, the lettered plates use only 5/6 the amount of metal.

14. Add the pence column (74d), divide by 12, write the remainder (2d) and carry the quotient (6s) to the shilling column. Then add this column (136s), divide by 20, write 16s and carry £6 to the pound column whose sum is then £11; and Jefferson is correct.

15. The number N will be of the binary form $n_k n_{k-1} \ldots n_1 0$, where the digits n_i are either 0 or 1. In the decimal system‡

$$N = n_k \times 2^k + n_{k-1} \times 2^{k-1} + \ldots + n \times 2 + 0 .$$

Since every term in this sum is divisible by 2, so is the sum; i.e. so is N.

---

† Suppose we have 10 symbols and we wish to make different plates using, say, 3 of these symbols. For the first symbol we may use any one of the original 10 symbols, and likewise for the second and third symbols. Therefore the number of different plates would be $10 \times 10 \times 10 = 1000$. (This subject matter is covered in discussions on permutations and combinations.)

‡ Powers are defined in the next section.

If M ends in 2 zeros then

$$M = m_r \times 2^r + \ldots + m_2 \times 2^2 + 0 \times 2 + 0,$$

and M is divisible by $2^2 = 4$. In general if the number ends in t zeros it will be divisible by 2^t. Note that in the decimal system (base 10), if a number ends in t zeros it is divisible by 10^t.

Set 5 (page 20)

1. $5^1 = 5$, $5^2 = 5 \times 5 = 25$, $5^3 = 5 \times 5^2 = 125$, $5^4 = 5 \times 5^3 = 625$,
$$5^5 = 5 \times 5^4 = 3125.$$

2. Since $1 \times 1 \times \ldots \times 1 = 1$, one to any power is one.

3. $(1.5)^1 = 1.5$, $(1.5)^2 = 2.25$, $(1.5)^3 = 3.375$, $(1.5)^4 = 5.0625$,
$$(1.5)^5 = 7.59375.$$

4. Since $0 \times 0 \times \ldots \times 0 = 0$, zero to any power is zero.

5. $2^7 = 128$, $7^2 = 49$; $4^3 = 64$, $3^4 = 81$.

6. 10^{100} written out has 100 zeros and 1 one, i.e., 101 symbols. In exponent form it has 5 symbols, a saving of 96 symbols.

7. $5^6 = 15,625$, $6^5 = 7,776$.

8. $2^{3+5} = 2^8 = 256$, $(3 + 5)^2 = 8^2 = 64$.

9. $2^7 =$ 128 has 3 digits
$2^{10} =$ 1,024 has 4 digits
$2^{14} =$ 16,384 has 5 digits
$2^{17} =$ 131,072 has 6 digits
$2^{20} = 1,048,576$ has 7 digits

By inspection, we see that the number of digits is about one third the exponent. By using logarithms this can be made more precise. The idea is to express the number 2^n as a number 10^k. If k is between 1 and 2, 10^k has 2 digits. If k is between 2 and 3, 10^k has 3 digits. In general if k is between $m - 1$ and m then 10^k has m digits. Set $10^k = 2^n$. Then $k \log_{10} 10 = n \log_{10} 2$. Since $\log_{10} 10 = 1$ and $\log_{10} 2 = .3010 \ldots$, we have $k = n \log_{10} 2 \approx .3010n$. Therefore the number of digits in 2^n equals the first integer greater than $n \log_{10} 2 \approx .3010n$. Example: $n = 17$, $.3010 \times 17 = 5.117$. The first integer greater than 5.117 is 6, and 2^{17} has six digits.

Set 6 (page 26)

1. $10,000,000,000 = 10^{10}$.

2. A million billion = a billion million = a quadrillion = 10^{15}.

3. $(3 \times 100) + 3 = 303$, so a centillion would be 10^{303}.

4. The number consists of 66 nines.

5. Reading from the left to the right we have a one, nine zeros, a one, nine zeros and a one.

7. Twelve quadrillion, three hundred forty-five trillion, six hundred seventy-eight billion, nine hundred million.

8. 6,500,000,000,000,000,000,000.

Set 7 (page 28)

1. a) $6^8 \times 6^{10} = 6^{8+10} = 6^{18}$.
   b) $6^8 \times 6^8 = 6^{8+8} = 6^{16}$ or $6^8 \times 6^8 = (6^8)^2 = 6^{16}$.
   c) $(6^8)^3 = 6^{24}$.
   d) $2^4 \times 4^2 = 2^4 \times (2^2)^2 = 2^4 \times 2^4 = 2^8$.

2. $100^{10} = (10^2)^{10} = 10^{20}$; $\therefore 10^{100} > 100^{10}$.
   $8^{16} = (2^3)^{16} = 2^{48}$, $16^8 = (2^4)^8 = 2^{32}$, $2^{48} > 2^{32}$.

3. $(2 + 5)^4 = 7^4 = 2401$, $2^4 + 5^4 = 16 + 625 = 641$.

4. $(1 + 2 + 3)^4 = 6^4 = 1296$, $1^4 + 2^4 + 3^4 = 1 + 16 + 81 = 98$.

5. Using the first law of exponents: $a^m \times (a^n \times a^p) = a^m \times a^{n+p}$. Let $n + p = r$ and use the first law again: $a^m \times a^r = a^{m+r}$. Substitute $n + p$ for r.

6. $(ab)^m = ab \times ab \times \ldots \times ab$ (m ab's multiplied together). Since we may change the order of the terms (we say that multiplication is commutative; i.e., $3 \times 2 = 2 \times 3$) we can write all the a's then all the b's: $(ab)^m = a \times \ldots \times a \times b \times \ldots \times b$ (m a's multiplied together followed by m b's multiplied together). But m a's multiplied together is a^m, m b's is b^m, and so we have $a^m b^m$.

7. Using the second law of exponents, $(a^m)^m = a^{m^2}$; using it again,
   $$[(a^m)^m]^m = (a^{m^2})^m = a^{m \cdot m^2} = a^{m^3}.$$

8. $2^{2^2} = 2^4 = 16$, $2^{2^3} = 2^8 = 256$, $3^{2^2} = 3^4 = 81$.

9. $3^{(2^3)} = 3^8$, $(3^2)^3 = 3^6$, $3^8 \neq 3^6$.

10. $2^{2^{2^2}} = 2^{16} = 65,536$.

Set 8 (page 30)

1. a) 3.65×10^2,   b) 1.0078×10^4,   c) 6.329480×10^6.
2. 2.5×10^9, 6.5×10^{12}.

Set 10 (page 33)

1. 372,950,   372,900,   373,000,   400,000.
2. 300,000.

5. The number has been rounded.

6. This number rounded to one significant figure is 3,000,000 which is its order of magnitude.

7. a) $2^{15} = 32{,}768 \approx 32{,}800 = 3.28 \times 10^4$.
   b) There are $(36)^3$ cubic inches in a cubic yard.
   $$36^3 = 46656 \approx 46700 = 4.67 \times 10^4.$$

Set 11 (page 36)

1. a) \$1.80 + \$10.80 + \$0.00 + \$9.20 = \$21.80 (nearest 10 cents).
   \$2.00 + \$11.00 + \$0.00 + \$9.00 = \$22.00 (nearest dollar).
   b) $70 \times 90 \times 40 = 7 \times 9 \times 4 \times 10^3 = 252 \times 10^3 \approx 3 \times 10^5$.

2. 5280 ft/mi $\times$ 12 in/ft $\approx 5300 \times 12 = 63{,}600 \approx 6.4 \times 10^4$ in/mi.
   (Rounded to 2 significant figures.)

3. 1 rod = 16.5 feet, 1 sq rod $\approx (16 \text{ ft})^2 = 256 \approx 2.6 \times 10^2$ sq ft.
   1 acre = 1.6×10^2 sq rods $\approx 1.6 \times 2.6 \times 10^4$ sq ft.
   $\quad = 4.16 \times 10^4 \approx 4.2 \times 10^4$ sq ft.   (Rounded to 2 significant figures.)

4. $\pi = 3.14 \ldots \approx 3.1$.
   Area $= \pi r^2 \approx 3.1 \times 120 \times 120 = 3.1 \times 1.2 \times 1.2 \times 10^4$
   $\quad\quad\quad \approx 3.1 \times 1.4 \times 10^4 = 4.34 \times 10^4$
   $\quad\quad\quad \approx 4.3 \times 10^4$ sq in. (Rounded to 2 significant figures.)

5. $\pi \approx 3$, radius = 18 in $\approx$ 20 in,
   Volume $= \frac{4}{3}\pi r^3 \approx \frac{4}{3} \times 3 \times 20 \times 20 \times 20 = 32 \times 10^3$
   $\quad\quad\quad\quad \approx 3 \times 10^4$ cu in. (Rounded to 1 significant figure.)

6. Approximately 2,000 years, approximately 50 Sundays to a year, therefore approximately 1×10^5 Sundays. (Rounded to one significant figure.)

7. To the nearest cent. Rounding occurs, for instance, when interest is computed.

8. Round all numbers to 1 significant figure.
   No. of seconds in a year
   $\approx 6 \times 10 \text{ sec/min} \times 6 \times 10 \text{ min/hr} \times 2 \times 10 \text{ hr/day} \times 4 \times 10^2 \text{ days/yr}$
   $\approx 288 \times 10^5 \approx 3 \times 10^7$ sec/yr.
   Thus the sun travels approximately
   $$3 \times 10 \text{ mi/sec} \times 3 \times 10^7 \text{ sec/yr} = 9 \times 10^8 \text{ mi/yr}.$$

9. Radius $\approx 4 \times 10^3$ miles, $(4 \times 10^3)^2 = 4^2 \times (10^3)^2 = 16 \times 10^6$,
   Area $= 4\pi r^2 \approx 12 \times 16 \times 10^6 = 192 \times 10^6 \approx 2 \times 10^8$ sq mi.

10. From Problem 4, 1 acre $\approx 4.2 \times 10^4$ sq ft, 1 sq ft $\approx 1.4 \times 10^2$ sq in.
    Therefore
    1 acre $\approx 1.4 \times 10^2 \times 4.2 \times 10^4 \approx 5.88 \times 10^6 \approx 5.9 \times 10^6$ sq in.
    Income/acre $\approx .25 \times 5.9 \times 10^6 \approx 1.475 \times 10^6 \approx \$1.5 \times 10^6$.

Set 12 (page 39)

6. A recent Washington, D.C. phone book lists 52 columns of Smiths out of a total of about 5400 columns. The ratio is therefore $\frac{52}{5400} \approx$ (say) $\frac{1}{100}$. (What is this ratio for your city?) Of course, the phone book lists businesses, offices, etc., and Washington may not be a typical city, but these figures would indicate that about 1 person in 100 is a Smith. At this rate there should be around 2,000,000 Smiths in the U.S.A.

8. The actual count (in the King James version) is supposed to be 2,728,800 for the Old Testament, 838,380 for the New Testament. Total: 3,567,180.

9. The Holland-America line estimates 36,855 pounds of meat, 9,250 pounds of fowl, and 11,560 pounds of fish.

Set 13 (page 43)

1. 4.0082×10^{-3}, 2.223×10^{-8}.

2. .0000000229,   .000030077.

3. 1 picogram $= 10^{-12}$ grams, 1 centigram $= 10^{-2}$ grams. Therefore 1 gram $= 10^{12}$ picograms $= 10^{2}$ centigrams, or, dividing by 10^{2}, 10^{10} picograms $= 1$ centigram.

4. $\frac{3}{127} = .02362\ldots$, $\frac{4}{169} = .02366\ldots$,   so $\frac{4}{169} > \frac{3}{127}$.

5. Find a common denominator for the fractions and compare the numerators:

$$\frac{3 \times 169}{127 \times 169}, \quad \frac{4 \times 127}{127 \times 169}$$

$$3 \times 169 = 507, \quad 4 \times 127 = 508, \quad 508 > 507.$$

6. Multiply numerator and denominator by the appropriate number so that all the denominators equal 64: $\frac{7}{64}''$, $\frac{8}{64}''$, $\frac{10}{64}''$, $\frac{16}{64}''$, $\frac{11}{64}''$, $\frac{12}{64}''$.

Arrange in order of size: $\frac{7}{64}''$, $\frac{8}{64}''$, $\frac{10}{64}''$, $\frac{11}{64}''$, $\frac{12}{64}''$, $\frac{16}{64}''$.

7. a) Since

$$\frac{1}{30} + \frac{1}{30} + \frac{1}{30} + \frac{1}{30} + \frac{1}{30} + \frac{1}{30} < \frac{1}{25} + \frac{1}{26} + \frac{1}{27} + \frac{1}{28} + \frac{1}{29} + \frac{1}{30}$$

$$< \frac{1}{25} + \frac{1}{25} + \frac{1}{25} + \frac{1}{25} + \frac{1}{25} + \frac{1}{25},$$

the answer is surely greater than $\frac{6}{30} = .20$ and less than $\frac{6}{25} = .24$. A good guess might be the average of these values: .22.

b) Exact answer: $\dfrac{1,560,647}{7,125,300} = .219028\ldots.$

Note the large numbers that arise from this "simple" addition.

Set 14 (page 46)

1. $2.72 \times 3.03 \times 10^{-5} \times 10^8 = 2.72 \times 3.03 \times 10^3 = 8.2416 \times 10^3$.

2. $\dfrac{1}{7^8}$ is larger than $\dfrac{1}{7^{16}}$.

3. $\quad 2^{-(2^3)} = 2^{-8} = \dfrac{1}{2^8} = \dfrac{1}{256}, \quad 2^{(2^3)} = 2^8 = 256,$

$\quad (-2)^{2^3} = (-2)^8 = (-1 \times 2)^8 = (-1)^8 \times (2)^8 = 256,$

$\quad (-2)^{-2^3} = \dfrac{1}{(-2)^{2^3}} = \dfrac{1}{256}.$

5. $\left(\dfrac{a}{b}\right)^m = \overbrace{\dfrac{a}{b} \times \ldots \times \dfrac{a}{b}}^{m \text{ factors}} = a \times \dfrac{1}{b} \times \ldots \times a \times \dfrac{1}{b}$, or

$\overbrace{a \times \ldots \times a}^{m \text{ factors}} \times \overbrace{\dfrac{1}{b} \times \ldots \times \dfrac{1}{b}}^{m \text{ factors}} = a^m \times \left(\dfrac{1}{b}\right)^m.$

6. One square fermi $= 10^{-13} \times 10^{-13} = 10^{-26}$ square centimeters

$= 10^{-26} \times 10^{-24}$ sq. cm. $= 10^{-2}$ barns,

or 1 barn $= 10^2$ sq. fermis.

Set 15 (page 50)

4. a) Choose the unit of length to be less than the length of the smaller object.
   b) Choose the unit length greater than the length of the larger object.
   c) Choose the unit length between the lengths of the two objects.

5. $\dfrac{L}{L} = I, \quad I \times L = I.$ Therefore $\left(\dfrac{L}{L}\right) \times L = I$.

6. $\dfrac{L}{S} = L, \left(\dfrac{L}{S}\right) \times S = L \times S = I; \left(\dfrac{S}{S}\right) = I, L \times \left(\dfrac{S}{S}\right) = L \times I = I$.

7. $S^2 = S \times S = S, \quad L^2 = L \times L = L, \quad I^2 = I \times I = I$.

8. $S^n = \overbrace{S \times S \times \ldots \times S}^{n \text{ factors}} = S, \quad L^n = \overbrace{L \times L \times \ldots \times L}^{n \text{ factors}} = L,$

$I^n = \overbrace{I \times \ldots \times I}^{n \text{ factors}} = I$.

9. This follows immediately from 8, for, e.g., S to any positive power is S; thus $S^m = S, S^n = S, S^{m+n} = S$, and

$$S^m \times S^n = S \times S = S = S^{m+n}.$$

10. Again, since $S^n = S$, $(S^n)^m = (S)^m = S$ and $S^{nm} = S^k$ (where $k = nm$) $= S$. (The same reasoning holds for L and I.) So the second law holds.

11. $\sqrt{S}$ designates the collection of numbers which is obtained by taking square roots of numbers in S. Since the square root of a number between 0 and 1 is itself between 0 and 1, and since, conversely, every number between 0 and 1 is the square root of some number between 0 and 1, we have $\sqrt{S} = S$. $\sqrt{L}$ and $\sqrt{I}$ can be defined in a similar way and we have $\sqrt{L} = L$, $\sqrt{I} = I$.   We might also observe that

$$S \times S = S^2 = S\,,$$

and so "extracting the square root" of both sides yields $S = \sqrt{S}$. Similar observations hold for L and I.

12. $a = S$, $b = L$.

$$S \times L = I\,, \qquad \sqrt{S \times L} = \sqrt{I} = I\,,$$
$$\sqrt{S} = S\,, \qquad \sqrt{L} = L\,, \qquad \sqrt{S} \times \sqrt{L} = S \times L = I\,.$$

Therefore $\qquad\qquad \sqrt{S \times L} = \sqrt{S} \times \sqrt{L}.$

The other possibilities are established in the same way. The rules hold.

Set 16 (page 54)

4. $9,999,999,999 \approx 10^{10}$. $\dfrac{10^{10}\ \text{subtractions}}{1300\ \text{subtractions/minute}} = \dfrac{10^8}{13}\ \text{min} \approx 15\ \text{years}.$

5. On some machines the motor will run indefinitely until it has been turned off by pressing a stop key.

Set 17 (page 65)

1. $3\frac{10}{71} = 3.1408\ldots$, $3\frac{1}{7} = 3.1428\ldots$; since $\pi = 3.14159\ldots$, it lies between $3\frac{10}{71}$ and $3\frac{1}{7}$, and agrees with these numbers to 2 decimal places.

2. By long division, $355/113 = 3.1415929\ldots$, but $\pi = 3.1415926\ldots$; the numbers agree to six places.

3. The average of $3\frac{1}{7}$ and $3\frac{10}{71}$ is (see Problem 1),

$\qquad \frac{1}{2}(3.1408\ldots + 3.1428\ldots) = \frac{1}{2}(6.2836\ldots) = 3.1418\ldots$.

π is closer to this average than to either number.

4. Radius of earth $\approx 4,000$ mi $\approx 2.53 \times 10^6$ in.,

circumference $\approx 1.58 \times 10^9$ in. $2^{30} \approx 1.07 \times 10^9$,

$$\frac{\text{circumference}}{2^{30}} \approx \frac{1.58 \times 10^9}{1.07 \times 10^9} \approx 1.5\ \text{in.}$$

5. $(3.14159265\ldots)^2 - 10 \approx -.13$

   $22(3.14159265\ldots)^4 - 2143 \approx .0000027$

   $9(3.14159265\ldots)^4 - 240(3.14159265\ldots)^2 + 1492 \approx -.023.$

6. $a = \frac{13}{64} \times 31{,}680 = 13 \times 495$ in. $\approx 13 \times 5 \times 10^2$ in.

   $b = \frac{11}{64} \times 31{,}680 = 11 \times 495$ in. $\approx 11 \times 5 \times 10^2$ in.

   area $= \pi ab \approx 3.1 \times 1.3 \times 1.1 \times 2.5 \times 10^7$ sq. in.

$$= \frac{3.1 \times 1.3 \times 1.1 \times 2.5 \times 10^7}{1.4 \times 10^2} \text{ sq. ft.}$$

$$\frac{3.1 \times 1.3 \times 1.1 \times 2.5 \times 10^7}{1.4 \times 4.4 \times 10^6} \text{ acres} \approx 18 \text{ acres.}$$

Set 18 (page 74)

1. We first define $n!$ (read n factorial).

$$n! = n \times (n - 1) \times (n - 2) \times \ldots \times 1,$$

that is, $1! = 1,\quad 2! = 2 \times 1 = 2,\quad 3! = 3 \times 2 \times 1 = 6.$

Then Liouville's number has a 1 in the $n!$ decimal place for $n = 1, 2, 3, \ldots$ and 0 elsewhere. Since the ones do not appear periodically the number is *not* a repeating decimal and so it is not a fraction. Since the only digits which appear are 0 and 1 the number is not normal.

2. 362 0's,   428 1's,   409 2's,   369 3's,   405 4's,

   418 5's,   398 6's,   376 7's,   405 8's,   430 9's.

If the digits were divided absolutely evenly there would be 400 of each.

3.

	Observed Frequency	Expected Frequency
Busts	115	$.2952 \times 400 = 118.08$
One Pair	198	$.5040 \times 400 = 201.6$
Two Pairs	53	$.1080 \times 400 = 43.2$
Three of a kind	28	$.0720 \times 400 = 28.8$
Full house	3	$.0090 \times 400 = 3.6$
Straight	2	$.0072 \times 400 = 2.88$
Four of a kind	1	$.0045 \times 400 = 1.8$
Five of a kind	0	$.0001 \times 400 = .04$

Set 19 (page 82)

1. $\frac{1}{13} = 0.076923\ldots,\quad \frac{1}{51} = 0.0196078431372549\ldots,$

  $\frac{1}{61} = 0.016393442622950819672131147540983606557377049180327868852459 01 \ldots.$

2. $10,000r = 2468.2468 \ldots$
   $r = .2468 \ldots$

   $9,999r = 2468,$ $r = \dfrac{2468}{9999}.$

3. $10,000r = 1961.1961 \ldots$
   $r = .1961 \ldots$

   $9,999r = 1961,$ $r = \dfrac{1961}{9999}.$

Set 20 (page 90)

1. The sum of the digits is 41, $4 + 1 = 5$; the number is not a square.

2. The sum of the digits is 36, $3 + 6 = 9$; this answer is admissible for a square, but this test does not suffice. By taking square roots, we obtain 1164 exactly.

3. Adding the digits as above the final answer is 9; this answer is admissible for a cube, but this test does not suffice. Taking cube roots, we obtain 1776 exactly.

4. Let s_1 and s_2 be two squares. Then $s_1 \times s_2$ is the square of the number $\sqrt{s_1} \times \sqrt{s_2}$. For example, let $s_1 = 4$, $s_2 = 9$, then $\sqrt{s_1} = 2$, $\sqrt{s_2} = 3$, $s_1 \times s_2 = 36$, $\sqrt{s_1} \times \sqrt{s_2} = 6$, $6^2 = 36$. In general, the product of n squares $s_1 \times \ldots \times s_n$ is the square of the number $\sqrt{s_1} \times \ldots \times \sqrt{s_n}$.

5. Let c_1 and c_2 be two cubes. Then $c_1 \times c_2$ is the cube of the number $\sqrt[3]{c_1} \times \sqrt[3]{c_2}$. The proof for the general case is the same.

6. We observe first that, if the number n^2 ends in an even digit, then n^2 is even. Moreover, n must be even because, if n were odd, say $n = 2m + 1$, then $n^2 = 4m^2 + 4m + 1 = 2[2m^2 + 2m] + 1$ would be odd and could not end in an even digit. Since n is divisible by 2, it is twice another number, say $n = 2k$. Hence $n^2 = 4k^2$ is divisible by 4.

7. If n^2 ends in a zero, then it is a multiple of 10, i.e. it has the factors 2 and 5. But the square n^2 must have all its prime factors repeated an even number of times (half of them come from the first n, the other half from the second n in n^2). So n^2 must have the factors $2^2 \times 5^2 = 100$, or $2^4 \times 5^4 = 10,000$, etc. and hence ends in an even number of zeros.

8. The smallest number divisible by $1, 2, \ldots, 9, 10$ is 2520 and the smallest number which we can raise to this power is 2, i.e., 2^{2520} is the number.

$$2^{2520} = (2^{1260})^2 = (2^{840})^3 = (2^{630})^4 = (2^{504})^5 = (2^{420})^6 = (2^{360})^7$$
$$= (2^{315})^8 = (2^{280})^9 = (2^{252})^{10}.$$

9. $1936 = 44^2$. The next year that is a square is $45^2 = 2025$.

10. $1728 = 12^3$. The next year that is a cube is $13^3 = 2197$.

11. 360,360 is divisible

by: since:

2   0 is divisible by 2

3    $3 + 6 + 0 + 3 + 6 + 0 = 18$ is divisible by 3

4    $12 + 0 = 12$ is divisible by 4

5   0 is divisible by 5

6   it is divisible by 2 and 3

7    $(3 \times 0) + (2 \times 6) - (1 \times 3) - (3 \times 0) - (2 \times 6) + (1 \times 3) = 0$ is divisible by 7

8    $0 + (2 \times 6) + (4 \times 3) = 24$ is divisible by 8

9    $3 + 6 + 3 + 6 = 18$ is divisible by 9

10   0 is the last digit

11    $0 - 6 + 3 - 0 + 6 - 3 = 0$ is divisible by 11

12   it is divisible by 4 and 3

13    $(10 \times 0) - (4 \times 6) - (1 \times 3) + (3 \times 0) + (4 \times 6) + (1 \times 3) = 0$ is divisible by 13.

12.

1	2	3	4	5	6	7	8	9	10	11	12	13
1	2	3	2^2	5	2×3	7	2^3	3^2	2×5	11	$2^2 \times 3$	13

Hence the least common multiple of the first 13 integers is

$$2^3 \times 3^2 \times 5 \times 7 \times 11 \times 13 = 360,360 .$$

13. For the number $10 \ldots 01$ to be divisible by 7, the sum

$$(3 \times 1) + (2 \times 0) - (1 \times 0) - (3 \times 0) - (2 \times 0) + (1 \times 0) + (3 \times 0) + \ldots + (n \times 1) ,$$

where n is one of the numbers $3, 2, -1, -3, -2, 1$, must be divisible by 7. But this sum is equal to $(3 \times 1) + (n \times 1)$ which is divisible by 7 only if $n = -3$. Thus the sequence must end with -3 so we can have 2 zeros, or we can add 6 more zeros until we come to -3 the second time, etc. So the possible number of zeros is given by $2 + 6m$ where m may be $1, 2, 3, \ldots$. The same type of reasoning proves the statement for divisibility by 13.

14. To test the given number consisting of n digits, all ones, for divisibility by 7, we cut off the sum

$$(3 \times 1) + (2 \times 1) - (1 \times 1) - (3 \times 1) - (2 \times 1) + \ldots$$

(where the dots indicate repetition of these terms) after n terms and find that, when $n = 1, 2, 3, 4, 5,$ or 6, the corresponding sum is 3, 5, 4, 1, -1, or 0. For $n = 7, 8, \ldots$, the values $3, 5, \ldots$ of the corresponding sums just repeat. The only one of these sums divisible by 7 is 0. Each time we have six 1's in a row the sum will be 0 so the number of 1's must be a multiple of 6. The same type of argument proves that this is also true for divisibility by 13.

15. $1 \times 2 \times 3 \times 4 \times \ldots \times 10 + 1 = 3{,}628{,}801$,

$$1 - 0 + 8 - 8 + 2 - 6 + 3 = 0 ,$$

and 0 is divisible by 11.

16. Let p be the prime, let 6 go into p n times with a remainder r where r may be 1, 2, 3, 4, or 5, i.e.,

$$\frac{p}{6} = n + \frac{r}{6} \quad \text{or} \quad p = 6n + r .$$

Now if r is a digit other than 1 or 5, the right side may be factored:

$$p = 6n + 2 = 2(3n + 1), \qquad p = 6n + 3 = 3(2n + 1),$$
$$p = 6n + 4 = 2(3n + 2),$$

and p will be divisible by 2, 3, or 4 and thus cannot be a prime.

17. We shall verify that 1951 and 1973 are primes by showing that they are not divisible by any of the primes $2, 3, 5, 7, \ldots$ The question is how far must we go to be sure? It will suffice to test all primes smaller than 45 because 45^2 is greater than both 1951 and 1973, and if 1951 had a factor greater than 45, then its other factor must be smaller than 45 and hence it lies among the primes we are testing. The same is true for 1973. Now we just verify that neither 1951 nor 1973 is divisible by 2, 3, 5, 7, 11, 13, 17, 19, 23, 29, 31, 37, 41, 43.

19. a) $1729 = 1728 + 1 \quad = 12^3 + 1^3$
$\qquad = 1000 + 729 = 10^3 + 9^3$.

b) $1, 8, 27, 64, 125, 216, 343, 512, 729, 1000, 1331, 1728$ are the cubes less than 1729; try all possibilities.

20. Let T be a triangular number. Then

$$T = 1 + 2 + \ldots + n = \frac{n}{2}(1 + n)$$

$$8T + 1 = \frac{8n}{2}(1 + n) + 1 \quad = 4n^2 + 4n + 1 = (2n + 1)^2 .$$

So $8T + 1$ is the square of the number $2n + 1$. Conversely, if $8N + 1$ is a square, it must be the square of an odd number: $8N + 1 = (2n + 1)^2$. Consequently $N = \frac{1}{2}n(1 + n)$ and hence must be triangular.

Set 21 (page 101)

1. Find the digit sums of the summands:

$1 + 2 + 9 + 5 = 17,$		$1 + 7 = 8;$
$2 + 8 + 7 + 2 = 19,$	$1 + 9 = 10,$	$1 + 0 = 1;$
$9 + 0 + 0 + 1 = 10,$		$1 + 0 = 1;$
$6 + 2 + 1 + 4 = 13,$		$1 + 3 = 4;$
$7 + 7 + 2 + 8 = 24,$		$2 + 4 = 6.$

Add these digit sums: $8 + 1 + 1 + 4 + 6 = 20,\ 2 + 0 = 2$.
Find the digit sum of the reputed sum: $6 + 4 + 2 = 12,\ 1 + 2 = 3$.
Since $3 \neq 2$, the sum is not correct; in fact the correct sum is 63920.

2. $1 + 6 + 9 + 2 + 0 + 2 + 0 + 3 + 0 + 2 + 0 + 2 + 0 + 1 = 28$, $2 + 8 = 10$, $1 + 0 = 1$ and the number is not a multiple of 9.

3. The sums of the individual digits in the two numbers are the same, and this sum is the remainder when the number is divided by 9 (provided that, if the sum exceeds 8, we replace it by its residue). The residue of the difference of two numbers is equal to the difference of their residues. (This may be proved in the same way as for the sum.) The difference of the residues of these two numbers is zero (since their residues are the same) and so this difference is divisible by 9.

4. To be divisible by 9 the sum of the digits must be a multiple of 9 and thus must contain at least 9 ones. The smallest such number is 111,111,111.

5. The $9 \times m$th term, $m = 1, 2, 3, \ldots$, has $9m$ sevens. The sum of the digits of this term is $9 \times m \times 7$ which is certainly divisible by 9. There are no other multiples of 9 in the series of digit sums.

6. Every 3rd term in the series of 6's is divisible by 9 since each time we add 3 sixes we add 18 to the sum of the digits and 18 is divisible by 9.

In the second series, consider separately the 1st, 3rd, 5th, ... terms

$$2, \qquad 252, \qquad 25252, \qquad \ldots,$$

and the 2nd, 4th, 6th, ... terms

$$25, \qquad 2525, \qquad 252525, \qquad \ldots.$$

The $(2m + 1)$st term consists of $(m + 1)$ 2's and m 5's. The $(2m)$th term consists of m 2's and m 5's. The digit sum of the $(2m + 1)$st term is therefore $2(m + 1) + 5m = 7m + 2$. The digit sum of the $2m$th term is $2m + 5m = 7m$. These must be multiples of 9. Now $7m$ is a multiple of 9 only when $m = 9, 18, \ldots$, i.e., a multiple of 9: $m = 9k$. $7m + 2$ is a multiple of 9 only if $m = 1, 10, 19, \ldots$, i.e., one more than a multiple of 9: $m = 9k + 1$. Thus, finally, the $2m = 2(9k) = 18k$th terms and the

$$2m + 1 = 2(9k + 1) + 1 = (18k + 3)\text{rd}$$

terms are the only multiples of 9 in the series. These are the 3rd, 18th, 21st, 36th, 39th, ... terms.

7. $r(79,532,853) = r(42) = 6$, $r(93,758,479) = r(52) = 7$, $r(6 \times 7) = r(42) = 6$, $r(7,456,879,327,810,587) = r(87) = r(15) = 6$, and the test is satisfied.

8. $r(123,456) = r(21) = 3$, $r(789,123) = r(30) = 3$, $r(3 \times 3) = 0$. $r(97,42d,969,088) = r(62 + d)$. We must have $r(62 + d) = 0$, i.e., $62 + d$ must be a multiple of 9, so $d = 1$.

9. $r(162,5d0,792) = r(32 + d)$. $32 + d$ must be a multiple of 9, so $d = 4$.

10. $r(6d,d23) = r(11 + 2d)$. $11 + 2d$ must be a multiple of 9, so $d = 8$.

Set 22 (page 114)

1. $2a + b = 99$ $2a + b = \quad 99$
    $a + 2b = 108$ $2a + 4b = \quad 216$

$$- 3b = -117 \qquad \text{1st reduced system}$$

$$b = 39$$

$$2a = 99 - 39 = 60, \qquad a = 30 \; .$$

2. $6x - y + z = \quad 8$ (1st equation)
    $6x + 30y - 6z = \quad 42$ (2nd equation)

$$- 31y + 7z = -34$$

$3x + 15y - 3z = 21$ (2nd equation)
$3x - 8y + 4z = \quad 3$ (3rd equation)

$$23y - 7z = 18$$

$-31y + 7z = -34$ 1st reduced system
$23y - 7z = \quad 18$

$$- 8y \quad = -16 \qquad \text{2nd reduced system}$$

$$y \quad = \quad 2$$

$-62 + 7z = -34$ $6x - 2 + 4 = 8$
$\quad 7z = -34 + 62 = 28$ $6x = 8 + 2 - 4 = 6$
$\quad z = \quad 4$ $x = 1 \; .$

3. As above, $-31y + 7z = -34$

$8x + 40y - 8z = 56$ (2nd equation)
$8x + 9y - z = 10$ (3rd equation)

$$31y - 7z = 46, \quad \text{or} \quad -31y + 7z = 46$$

$-31y + 7z = -34$ 1st reduced system
$-31y + 7z = \quad 46$

$$0 = -80 \; .$$

But this last equation is impossible and the given system of equations has no solution. In this case the system is called *inconsistent*. Inconsistent systems place contradictory requirements upon the unknowns.

4. We note that if we rewrite the 9 equations replacing G by I, I by G, etc. (as indicated in the problem) we obtain the same set of equations, and so $G = I$, etc. Physically we should expect that the average temperature at points which occupy positions symmetric with respect to the center line (CW) of the square will be equal. We have eliminated the 3rd, 6th and 9th equations since they are equal respectively to the 1st, 4th and 7th.

$$
\begin{aligned}
(1)\ 4I &= H + N + 200 \\
(2)\ 4H &= 2I + M + 100 \\
(3)\ 4N &= I + M + S + 100 \\
(4)\ 4M &= 2N + H + R \\
(5)\ 4S &= N + R + 140 \\
(6)\ 4R &= 2S + M + 40
\end{aligned}
$$

$$
\begin{array}{ll}
(1) & 4I - H \qquad\quad - N = 200 \\
(2) & \underline{-4I + 8H - 2M \qquad\quad = 200} \\
(7) & \qquad\quad 7H - 2M - N = 400
\end{array}
\qquad
\begin{array}{ll}
(1) & 4I - H \qquad\qquad\qquad -N = 200 \\
(3) & \underline{-4I \qquad - 4M - 4S + 16N = 400} \\
(8) & \qquad -H - 4M - 4S + 15N = 600
\end{array}
$$

Equations (4), (5), (6), (7), (8) are the 1st reduced system.

$$
\begin{array}{ll}
(4) & -7H + 28M - 14N - 7R = 0 \\
(7) & \underline{\ 7H - \ 2M - \ \ N \qquad\quad = 400} \\
(9) & \qquad 26M - 15N - 7R = 400
\end{array}
\qquad
\begin{array}{ll}
(4) & -H + 4M \qquad - 2N - R = \qquad 0 \\
(8) & \underline{-H - 4M - 4S + 15N \qquad = \ \ 600} \\
(10) & \qquad 8M + 4S - 17N - R = -600
\end{array}
$$

Equations (5), (6), (9), (10) are the 2nd reduced system.

$$
\begin{array}{ll}
(5) & 4S - N - \ R \qquad\quad = 140 \\
(6) & \underline{-4S \qquad + 8R - 2M = \ 80} \\
(11) & \quad - N + 7R - 2M = 220
\end{array}
\qquad
\begin{array}{ll}
(5) & 4S - \quad N - R \qquad\quad = \quad 140 \\
(10) & \underline{4S - 17N - R + 8M = -600} \\
(12) & \qquad 16N \qquad - 8M = \quad 740 \\
& \qquad \ 4N \qquad - 2M = \quad 185
\end{array}
$$

Equations (9), (11), (12) are the 3rd reduced system.

$$
\begin{array}{ll}
(9) & -7R + 26M - 15N = 400 \\
(11) & \underline{\ 7R - \ 2M - \quad N = 220} \\
& \qquad 24M - 16N = 620 \\
(13) & \qquad \ 6M - \ 4N = 155
\end{array}
\qquad
\begin{array}{ll}
(12) & \ 4N - 2M = 185 \\
(13) & \underline{-4N + 6M = 155} \\
& \qquad 4M = 340 \\
& \qquad \ M = \ 85
\end{array}
\quad
\begin{array}{l}
\text{4th reduced} \\
\text{system}
\end{array}
$$

Having determined M, we determine the other unknowns by back substitution:

$$
(13)\ 4N = 6 \times 85 - 155 = 355, \qquad N = \frac{355}{4};
$$

$$
(11)\ 7R = \frac{355}{4} + 170 + 220 = \frac{1915}{4}, \qquad R = \frac{1915}{28};
$$

$$
(10)\ 4S = -8 \times 85 + 17 \times \frac{355}{4} + \frac{1915}{28} - 600
$$

$$
= \frac{8320}{28} = \frac{2080}{7},
$$

$$
S = \frac{2080}{28} = \frac{520}{7};
$$

$$
(7)\ 7H = 400 + 2 \times 85 + \frac{355}{4} = \frac{2635}{4}, \qquad H = \frac{2635}{28};
$$

$$
(1)\ 4I = \frac{2635}{28} + \frac{355}{4} + 200 = \frac{2680}{7}, \qquad I = \frac{670}{7}.
$$

Therefore

$$
G = I = \frac{670}{7} \approx 95.7, \quad H = \frac{2635}{28} \approx 94.1, \quad L = N = \frac{355}{4} = 88.75,
$$

$$
M = 85, \qquad Q = S = \frac{520}{7} \approx 74.3, \qquad R = \frac{1915}{28} \approx 68.4.
$$

Set 23 (page 125)

1. The general term of sequence (A) is $100 + 1{,}000n$, that of sequence (B), $3^n \times 2$. We want to know when

$$\text{the ratio } \frac{3^n \times 2}{100 + 1{,}000n}$$

of the two terms is at least 1. This ratio will be greater than 1 for n greater than or equal to 8, i.e. beginning with the 9th term.

2. The general term of the ratios is $\dfrac{n}{\sqrt{n}}$. Multiplying this by $1 = \sqrt{n}/\sqrt{n}$ we have

$$\frac{n}{\sqrt{n}} = \frac{n\sqrt{n}}{n} = \sqrt{n}.$$

As n becomes larger and larger, so does $\sqrt{n}$.

3. The two ratios to be considered are

$$\frac{n\sqrt{n}}{n} = \sqrt{n} \quad \text{and} \quad \frac{n^2}{n\sqrt{n}} = \frac{n}{\sqrt{n}} = \sqrt{n}\,.$$

As n becomes larger, so does $\sqrt{n}$.

4. The general term is $n^{n^{\cdot^{\cdot^{\cdot^n}}}}$ (n n's). There are infinitely many sequences with more rapid growth. Consider for example the sequence with general term $\left(n^{n^{\cdot^{\cdot^n}}}\right)^2$. Then the ratio of the 2nd scale to the 1st is $n^{n^{\cdot^{\cdot^n}}}$ which increases as n increases.

5. The number of ancestors n generations removed is 2^n.

6. 2^{40}. The population wasn't this large ($2^{40} > 10^{12} = $ one trillion). This shows that people intermarry; for the answer to Problem 5 is correct only if the ancestors are all different.

8. 1 2 3 5 8 13   21   34   55   89   144   233 . . .
   1 2 3 5 8   13   21   34   55   89   144 . . .   1st differences

Taking growth differences again and again always gives us the Fibonacci sequence, i.e., none of the growths ever stops growing. On the other hand the nth difference of the scale of nth power is a constant, and hence this scale grows less rapidly than the Fibonacci sequence. The ratios of successive terms are:

$$\frac{2}{1} = 2\,, \quad \frac{3}{2} = 1.5\,, \quad \frac{5}{3} = 1.66\ldots, \quad \frac{8}{5} = 1.60\,, \quad \frac{13}{8} = 1.625\,,$$

$$\frac{21}{13} = 1.615\ldots, \frac{34}{21} = 1.619\ldots, \frac{55}{34} = 1.617\ldots, \frac{89}{55} = 1.618\ldots \text{ etc}$$

Notice that beginning with the first ratio every other term is greater than

$$\tfrac{1}{2}(1 + \sqrt{5}) = 1.618034\ldots$$

while the in between terms are less than it; but as we go on in the sequence, the terms come closer and closer to this "limit."

Miscellaneous Problems (page 127)

1. HUNDRED represents the number

$$7(26)^6 + 20(26)^5 + 13(26)^4 + 3(26)^3 + 17(26)^2 + 4(26) + 3.$$

THOUSAND begins with $19(26)^7$ and is therefore even larger.

MILLION is

$$12(26)^6 + 8(26)^5 + 11(26)^4 + 11(26)^3 + 8(26)^2 + 14(26) + 13.$$

Hence THOUSAND > MILLION > HUNDRED

$$\text{ONE} + \text{ONE} = 2[14(26)^2 + 13(26) + 4] = 28(26)^2 + (26)^2 + 8$$
$$= (26)^3 + 3(26)^2 + 8 = \text{BDAI}.$$

3. Area (circle) $= \pi r^2 \approx 3.14 \times 10^2$ sq. in. The screen forms small squares; the area of each is $\frac{1}{11} \times \frac{1}{11} = (\frac{1}{11})^2$ sq. in. Hence the circle contains approximately $3.14 \times 10^2 \times 11^2 \approx 38{,}000$ small squares. Each of these has $\frac{2}{11}$ in. of wire in it. (We allow only two adjacent sides so as to prevent counting double from square to square.) Hence there are approximately

$$3.14 \times 10^2 \times 11^2 \times \tfrac{2}{11} = 3.14 \times 10^2 \times 22 \approx 6{,}900 \text{ inches of wire }.$$

7. Number the particles

$$1, 2, 3, 4, \ldots, \qquad \tfrac{3}{2} \times 136 \times 2^{256},$$

and let i be the number of the particle we are trying to guess. We first find in which half of this set of numbers i lies by asking, say, "does i lie in the second half of this set?" Next we find in which half of this half, i.e. in which quarter of the original set, i lies. Proceeding in this way, the 264th question will tell us in which $(1/2)^{264}$ part of the original set i lies. Now we notice that

$$\frac{(3/2) \times 136 \times 2^{256}}{2^{264}} = \frac{(3/2) \times 17 \times 2^3 \times 2^{256}}{2^{264}} = \frac{3 \times 17}{2^6} = \frac{51}{64} < 1 .$$

So after the 264th guess we have less than one particle left and we have found the particle.

9. We notice, by considering successive powers of 3, that the last digit, d, forms a repeating sequence $1, 3, 9, 7, 1, 3, 9, \ldots.$ Consider any nonnegative power of 3, say 3^m. We may write $m = 4n + r$ where $n = 0, 1, 2, \ldots$, and $r = 0, 1, 2$ or 3. Then if $r = 0$, $d = 1$; if $r = 1$, $d = 3$; if $r = 2$, $d = 9$; and if $r = 3$, $d = 7$. For the number 3^{1001}, $m = 1001$, $n = 250$, $r = 1$ and so the last digit is 3. To find the 1st digit, we use logarithms.

$$\text{Log}_{10} 3^{1001} = 1001 \log_{10} 3 = 1001 \times .47712 = 477.59 \ldots ;$$

using anti-logarithms, we find that $3^{1001} = 303 \ldots$, i.e., the first digit is 3.

Bibliography

(S): Contains material appropriate to students.
(T): Contains material appropriate to teachers.
(A): Contains advanced mathematical material.

HISTORY OF MATHEMATICS

Smith, D. E., *History of Mathematics*, Dover reprint, New York, 1958. Though not up to date, this is particularly good for elementary work. Contains many illustrations. (S,T)

van der Waerden, B. L., *Science Awakening*, Nordhoff, Gröningen, 1954. A history of mathematics in antiquity. An exquisite book. (S,T)

WEIGHTS AND MEASURES

Judson, L. V., *Units and Systems of Weights and Measures. Their Origin, Development, and Present Status*, National Bureau of Standards Circular 570, U. S. Government Printing Office, Washington 25, D. C., 1956. (S, T)

MATHEMATICAL FALLACIES

Maxwell, E. A., *Fallacies in Mathematics*, Cambridge University Press, Cambridge, 1959. A collection of fallacious arguments in algebra, geometry, trigonometry, and calculus. (S, T)

163

HISTORY OF π

Hobson, E., *Squaring the Circle*, Chelsea reprint, New York, 1958. The story to the end of the 19th Century. (S, T)

REPEATING DECIMALS

Rademacher, H and Toeplitz, O., *The Enjoyment of Mathematics*, Princeton University Press, Princeton, 1947. Section 23. Selections from mathematics for the somewhat advanced amateur. (T, A) While many textbooks on algebra or higher algebra have a chapter on repeating decimals, Rademacher and Toeplitz go beyond the usual treatment.

IRRATIONAL NUMBERS, TRANSCENDENTAL NUMBERS, NORMAL NUMBERS

Niven, I., *Numbers: Rational and Irrational*, The New Mathematical Library, Vol. 1, 1961 (S, T)

Niven, I., *Irrational Numbers*, The Carus Mathematical Monographs, No. 11, 1956. (T, A)

GEOMETRIC CONSTRUCTIONS

Dickson, L. E., *First Course in the Theory of Equations*, Wiley, New York, 1921, Chapter III. (T, A)

Bieberbach, L., *Theorie der Geometrischen Konstruktionen*, Birkhäuser, Basel, 1952. (A)

ELECTRONIC COMPUTING MACHINERY

From among the many books on this topic, we select the following as being most suitable for this bibliography:

McCormick, E. M., *Digital Computer Primer*, McGraw-Hill, New York, 1959. (S, T)

THE THEORY OF NUMBERS

Uspensky, J. V. and Heaslet, M. A., *Elementary Number Theory*, McGraw-Hill, New York, 1939. (T)

Ore, O., *Number Theory and Its History*, McGraw-Hill, New York, 1948 (T)

PRIME NUMBERS

Lehmer, D. N., *List of Prime Numbers from 1 to 10,006,721*, Hafner reprint, New York, 1956. Contains an informative introduction on the history of the prime number problem. (S, T, A)

LARGE NUMBERS IN THE THEORY OF NUMBERS

Those interested will find much material in the back issues of the periodical *Mathematical Tables and Other Aids to Computation*, 1943–   . This periodical is currently entitled, *Mathematics of Computation*. (S, T, A)

SYSTEMS OF SIMULTANEOUS LINEAR EQUATIONS

Though all books on algebra contain chapters devoted to this topic, the reader may be interested in seeing this material against the wider backdrop of computational problems.

Milne, W. E., *Numerical Calculus*, Princeton University Press, Princeton, 1949, Chapter I. (T, A)

Kunz, K. S., *Numerical Analysis*, McGraw-Hill, New York, 1957, Chapter 10. (T, A)

GROWTH IN MATHEMATICS

Sawyer, W. W., *What Is Calculus About?* The New Mathematical Library, Vol. 2, 1961. (S, T)

All texts on calculus contain pertinent material in their chapters on sequences, limits, and indeterminate forms. (T) For the ideas of P. Dubois-Reymond and for the "algebra" of growth see:

Hardy, G. H., *Orders of Infinity*, Cambridge University Press, Cambridge, 2nd edition, 1954. (A)

Borel, E., *Leçons sur la théorie de la croissance*, Paris, 1910. (A)

GROWTH AND FORM IN NATURE

Thompson, D. W., *Growth and Form*, Cambridge University Press, Cambridge, 2nd edition, 1954. A classic. The illustrations alone are fascinating and should be highly suggestive. (S, T)

Kovach, L. D., "Life Can Be So Nonlinear," *American Scientist*, June 1960, pp. 218–225. An entertaining and instructive little article. (S, T)

Apropos of the size of Gargantua (Section 12) the reader might like to look at the essay "On Being the Right Size" which appears in Haldane, J. B. S., *Possible Worlds*, New York, 1928. (S, T)

LARGE NUMBERS AND ASTRONOMY

Gamow, G., *1, 2, 3, Infinity,* Viking, New York, 1957. (S, T)

Shapley, H., *Of Stars and Men*, Washington Square Press, New York, 1958. (S, T)

GENERAL

James and James, *Mathematics Dictionary*, Princeton, 1959. Contains many interesting little essays as part of the definitions. (S, T, A)

Kasner, E. and Newman, J., *Mathematics and the Imagination,* Simon & Schuster, New York, 1940, 1945. Popular essays. (S, T)

Littlewood, J. E., *A Mathematician's Miscellany*, Methuen, London, 1953. Mathematical nuggets by one of England's leading mathematicians. (S, T, A)